ATMOSPHERIC RAILWAYS
A Victorian Venture in Silent Speed

ATMOSPHERIC RAILWAYS

A Victorian Venture in Silent Speed

by

CHARLES HADFIELD

ALAN SUTTON
1985

Alan Sutton Publishing Limited
30 Brunswick Road
Gloucester GL1 1JJ

First published 1967
This edition published 1985

British Library Cataloguing in Publication Data

Hadfield, Charles
 Atmospheric railways
 1. Railroads, Atmospheric   2. Railroads—
 Great Britain
 I. Title
 385'.0941   TF692

 ISBN 0-86299-204-4

Printed and bound in Great Britain.

Newton Abbot Devon

CONTENTS

LIST OF ILLUSTRATIONS

PLATES

facing page

7

TEXT ILLUSTRATIONS

PREFACE

MY mother was born in Exeter, and as a girl lived beside the estuary of the Exe, looking across to the line of railway that runs down towards Dawlish Warren. Her father was an Exeter architect, her uncle a local clergyman, when the South Devon Railway was built; while reading local newspaper files to write this book, I came across many references to my great-uncle, who seems to have caused quite a stir in his parish.

She had probably heard of the atmospheric railway from her father or uncle, who may indeed have travelled on it, for when I was a boy she told me of it, and showed me the old engine-house at Starcross. Then and there I decided one day to find out all I could about it. Not long ago the opportunity came, and here is the result.

CHARLES HADFIELD

PUBLISHERS' NOTE

Starcross Pumping Station, nr. Exeter, Devon

Since this book was first published, the Atmospheric Pumping House at Starcross has been privately restored and opened to the public as an Independent Museum. Mr and Mrs R.A. Forrester bought the building from British Rail in 1981 and have constructed within it a working atmospheric railway in 15″ gauge, which regularly carries passengers weighing over 20 stone, and is powered by ordinary domestic vacuum cleaners which simulate, on a smaller scale, the effect of the original steam powered machinery. Artefacts from the South Devon Atmospheric Railway are displayed together with copies of original drawings and correspondence, and a sophisticated audio visual show tells the story. The stairway inside the unusual chimney has been made safe and a viewing platform constructed on top giving commanding views of Brunel's original broad gauge track bed and of the Exe Estuary.

Part One

RISE AND FALL OF AN IDEA

CHAPTER ONE

THE ATMOSPHERIC RAILWAY

HISTORY makes us all travellers in time. So let us go back to the summer of 1846, only sixteen years after the Liverpool & Manchester Railway had opened, and rather over five since the completion of the Great Western's main line from London to Bristol. The steam locomotive has developed greatly since the days of the *Rocket*, but it is still rather unreliable, dirty, heavy in relation to its power, and not yet able to face gradients of over 1 in 75 with well-loaded trains without help. It is leader of the traction field, but not yet supreme. Rope haulage is used on the London & Blackwall commuter line, and now another competitor has appeared, for Samuel Clegg and Joseph and Jacob Samuda have successfully harnessed the power of the atmosphere, and such engineers as Charles Vignoles, William Cubitt, and Isambard Kingdom Brunel are building railways of quite a new kind. Instead of locomotives, lineside steam engines provide power—enough power, it seems likely, to run intensive, regular-interval, cheap trains, clean, silent, and free from the possibility of collision. People of the eighteen-forties were offered the kind of train service that electric traction now gives to us. How could they not be fascinated?

We are standing beside an atmospheric railway, perhaps the London & Croydon between Forest Hill and Norwood, waiting for a train to pass. As progressive nineteenth-century people, we take a keen interest in mechanical inventions and have read descriptions of the new system. Now we have come to see how the thing works, and examine its construction closely. Then, if we think it safe, we are prepared to take a ride. A 15 in diameter cast-iron tube, laid in ten-foot lengths, lies between the rails, and is spiked to sleepers through cast-iron feet. The fins that run from one side of the tube round underneath and up the other side are there to strengthen it, and by setting them to lie against the edges of the sleepers both tube and track are given greater stability.

Each tube has a slot at the top about 2 in wide, set within a valve seating about $7\frac{1}{2}$ in across. An iron rib is cast on one side of the seating, to which is bolted one edge of the oxhide flexible valve that closes the slot to make the tube airtight. The leather is single where it lies over the part of the seating near the hinge and over the first part of the slot, but is doubled over the remainder of the slot and up to its far edge, which rests on the far channelled edge of the seating. Above the second strip of leather a series of thin iron plates 8 in long are riveted, which prevent the leather being forced down into the tube by external air pressure, and upon which runs the pressing wheel.*

Because the plates are short, they allow the leather valve to be pushed up sideways on its hinge from below, flexibly and without stiffness, and then to fall back. When the valve is shut the weight of the iron plates keeps the leather pressed on to its channel. This is filled with a mixture of beeswax and tallow which is solid at ordinary temperatures, and therefore makes an airtight seal between the leather valve and the iron tube.

Suddenly, as we stand beside the track, a gentle hissing noise approaches along the tube, passes, and fades into the distance. It tells us that the stationary steam engines placed every two or three miles alongside the line and working big air-pumps, have started to exhaust air from the tube, so causing some from outside to find its way past the seal. Even when the valve is in good

---

* What is described is the final form of the valve on the Croydon line, much simplified from the original invention. In this, the hinged edge of the leather valve was held between the tube and an iron bar running above it, and bolted down; the second leather strip and iron plate above it ran the full width of the slot opening and to the far channelled edge of the seating. Beneath the leather valve another iron plate was riveted, which also fitted the slot, and was made convex to conform to the shape of the tube.

condition, there is a little leakage, which increases as the vacuum rises.

We watch for the train. Six or seven minutes later we can see it coming—smokeless, nearly silent, without a locomotive, the driver standing at the front of the six-wheeled leading or piston carriage, his hand on the brake handle. His passengers are behind a partition, with others in the following carriages. As the express shoots past at over 60 mph, we hear the echoing rumble of air rushing into the opened valve, and then the sharp rattle of the smooth steel pressing wheel passing over iron plates to close it again. Then it is gone, and to all appearance the tube and valve are as before. The power of the atmosphere alone has driven the train, and the marvel of it compels us to believe that our generation has discovered the power secret of the future.

For our first ride, let us visit the seaside, and take a ticket for Teignmouth on one of the broad-gauge atmospheric trains of the South Devon leaving Exeter on the twenty-mile run to Newton* in the spring of 1848. The line starts at Exeter St Davids station, shared with the Bristol & Exeter company. The South Devon portion is a separate building, square, white-painted with a slate roof topped by a cupola, its entrance portico supported on slender pillars, the train shed behind. There are intermediate stations at Exeter St Thomas, Starcross, Dawlish, and Teignmouth, and engine-houses at Exeter, Countess Wear, Turf, Starcross, Dawlish, Teignmouth, Summerhouse near Bishopsteignton, and Newton. We can see the house at Exeter, just outside the station to the left of the carriage sheds and the right of the track, built in red Devon sandstone with a tiled roof. There is a good deal of smoke coming from its chimney, for Mr James Pearson, the manager of the atmospheric services, has been working his engines heavily, and is using coal instead of the more expensive anthracite or coke, as he ought.

The train of three carriages is waiting, and a number of men are pushing the piston carriage past them to take its place at the

* The station was not called Newton Abbot until 1877.

front. It is backed on and coupled up, and the driver in his greatcoat carrying the South Devon company's initials climbs to his platform. If we peer underneath, we can see the piston pointing towards the mouth of the main tube at the near end of Exe bridge. Here we have auxiliary starting equipment;* if we had been on the Dalkey, the train would have been pushed forward by hand until the piston had passed the valve, and would then have been held on the brakes.

We are waiting for the connecting train from Taunton, and it is late. The Bristol & Exeter has no telegraph, and herein lies one of Mr Brunel's troubles, for those engine-houses down the line which are still without it will start pumping according to the timetable, and must keep going until the train, however late it may be, arrives. Not too late this time, however, for its roar can be heard in the distance.

Ahead of the piston-carriage, between the track and the platform, stands a vacuum gauge connected at its foot to the main tube; on it we can read the slow increase of vacuum as the air-pumps labour. Normal working vacuum is about 16 in of mercury, giving 8 psi on the piston, using a 15 in tube, as we have here. A similar gauge is placed above the driver's seat. Countess Wear engine is exhausting the Exeter–Countess Wear section of tube; Turf engine that to Turf; and so on. Our engines at Exeter are not normally needed for a down train. Each engine pumps to the same vacuum, and each comes into service a prearranged number of minutes before the train's scheduled time of arrival. Normally, engines should pump for about five minutes to get the required vacuum.

The Bristol & Exeter train is in, and passengers are changing to the atmospheric line. Peering out of our second-class window in the piston-carriage, we notice a smaller 8 in tube between the rail and the platform, connected to the main tube ahead of us. In front of the train a rope is fastened to a shackle and bolt, which in turn is linked to a piston inside the tube, the other end

* This is assumption. Such equipment was installed at Starcross, Dawlish, and Teignmouth. It probably was at Exeter.

I. (above) Medhurst's pneumatic road carriage, driven by a piston working in a square tube; (below) Pilbrow's system of atmospheric traction, whereby a piston passing along a sunken tube turned spindles, the upper ends of which engaged a rack beneath the train

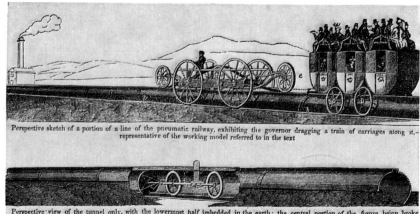

Perspective sketch of a portion of a line of the pneumatic railway, exhibiting the governor dragging a train of carriages along it,—representative of the working model referred to in the text

Perspective view of the tunnel only, with the lowermost half imbedded in the earth; the central portion of the figure being broke away to show the pneumatic piston; its attachment to the dynamic traveller, and the connexion of the latter by the vertical bar *f* to th governor, on the outside, seen in *Fig.* 1, at *g*.

II.   (above) The principle of Pinkus's atmospheric railway, using a rope valve, a piston or governor on wheels, and running rails integral with the tube; (centre) Pinkus's rope valve; (below) Hallette's tube, showing the coulter held between two small flexible tubes filled with compressed air

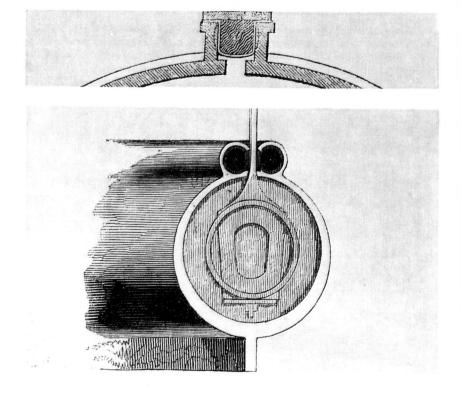

being hooked to a bar projecting from the side of the piston carriage.*

Our signal clears, the station bell rings, the guard blows his horn, and a porter opens the valve to admit air to the 8 in tube. The auxiliary piston starts forward, dragging our train behind it. The driver pulls in the bar to drop the starting rope, there is a bang beneath our carriage as the train piston passes the entrance valve of the main tube, and with a surge the train accelerates as it is driven forward. The driver has no control over this power, though he knows what vacuum he has in the tube from the gauge beside him. He can slow the train with his brake—but he can do nothing to get greater speed than the engine-house is giving him.

The driver and guard screw down their brakes for St Thomas's, and hold the train at the platform against the air pressure in the tube. No starting gear is therefore needed, and as they release their brakes the train drives forward. At Countess Wear, three miles from Exeter, we see the engine-house on the up side, with its reservoir behind it. Bang! The piston leaves the first section of tube. Bang! It enters the next; $2\frac{1}{2}$ miles to Turf, and a passenger balances a half-penny on its edge on the sill of his window, and watches it, fascinated. Turf engines, this time on the down side. Bang! Bang! The half-penny falls over, and we suddenly slow down. Evidently Starcross is having engine trouble, and has failed to get its proper vacuum. More slowly we run beside the Exe, till we hear the piston leave the tube; we swing to the left of the loop, and stop at Starcross station. Passengers for the ferry to Exmouth get out, and one or two locals. Clouds of smoke are coming from the engine-house on the up side just beyond the station : the Starcross engineman is determined that he will have full vacuum for the coming up train.

A porter attaches the starting rope, and we are off. As we enter the main tube beyond the points, the train leaps forward, and opposite us a market basket, fortunately empty, comes off the rack on to its owner's lap. In the confusion we hardly notice

* The method of fastening the rope to the train is conjectural.

B

the speed. Thanks to the steadying effect of the piston, we are taking the Warren curve fast, and flash along beside the sea-wall and the posts carrying the Electric Telegraph Company's wires, until the driver begins to screw down his brake for Dawlish. But he has not been quite quick enough. The train has passed the engine-house on the up side, overshot the train shed, and stopped beside the wooden platform extension that Mr Brunel has had to provide at intermediate stations since he found how difficult it is to stop an atmospheric train at exactly the right place. Again the train is started with a rope. Away through the tunnels, winding round by beach and cove, to emerge on the sea-wall, before swinging away to the approach tunnel* to the station and passing place at Teignmouth. Here also the engine-house is on the up side.

Having alighted, we wait to watch. An up goods train has just arrived, and is waiting at the other platform. The tubes in each direction are full of the air which has brought their trains to Teignmouth. That ahead of us is now being exhausted by the engines further down the line at Summerhouse, that over which we have just travelled by Dawlish. The porters attach the starting ropes, the signals turn, the drivers watch their gauges. Satisfied with the vacuum, the drivers signal to their guards, release their brakes, and the trains start to move. We hear the thud of each piston entering its tube, and watch the trains until they are out of sight. There are difficulties in this new system of locomotion, we have been told, but Mr Brunel is a clever engineer, and maybe he can surmount them after all.

Four atmospheric railways, totalling some 30 miles of single track, were built and operated: the earliest opened in 1844, the last closed in 1860. The system was practical, and it worked, though too many details needed perfecting to make it efficient; but it was expensive to build, and in many ways operationally inconvenient. Though it failed, however, yet it partially succeeded, for it first provided a fast, cheap, frequent and clean

* Later removed.

urban commuter rail service; it caused the first experimental underground tube lines to be built in Britain and the United States; and out of it came pneumatic systems of message transmission that are still useful today.

The five chapters that follow describe the rise and fall of the idea of atmospheric traction, the next five the building and working of the four railways. The last includes a number of practical matters of operation, and has something to say about the stationary engines: it can be skipped by the non-technical reader. Finally, an appendix gathers together the lines that were built or authorised, and some of those projected.

CHAPTER TWO

BEGINNINGS

THE story of those who first discovered and applied the force of the atmosphere is told in L. T. C. Rolt's *Thomas Newcomen: the Prehistory of the Steam Engine.** They were concerned with power, though one of them, Denis Papin (1647–1712) proposed to use an air-pump driven by a water-wheel to operate an atmospheric engine at a distance by means of a pipeline; in another form, as a means of exhausting the tube of an atmospheric railway, the use of a waterwheel or reservoir was suggested later by Samuda and Brunel. But it was Medhurst who stimulated the thought that eventually led to a practical railway.

George Medhurst, born in 1759 at Shoreham, Kent, was an engaging character who manufactured scales in Denmark Street, Soho, but in his spare time invented uses for compressed air. He took out his first patent in 1799 and followed it with others, including one in 1801 for a washing machine, but we are especially concerned with three. A pamphlet of 1810 explained *A New Method of conveying Letters and Goods with great certainty and rapidity by Air.* He claimed that letters could be sent through a small tube at 100 mph, and went on to apply the same principle to convey goods in trucks running on rails within an iron tube 12 sq ft in area, power being provided by a steam engine.

By 1812 his ideas had grown. He now proposed twin iron tubes 6 ft high by 5 ft wide, within which carriages having an inch clearance all round the tube might run on rails, carrying goods or passengers. He considered that the pressure inside the tube

* David & Charles, 1963.

need be very small, and could be provided by one 180 hp steam engine every ten miles. At these stations the carriages would come out of the tube, being braked by a rising slope, and would then be moved by a rope and windlass into the next.

At this point he seems to have reflected (not having clearly foreseen the days of the Underground) that passengers might not take too kindly to the inside of a tube so small, so dark, and so long, and added that it would be possible to put the carriage outside it. If so, there should be a 12 in diameter iron tube 'having a moving box or piston to fit and move freely within side, and made to communicate by a particular contrivance through the side of that tube to the carriage without, it will be impelled . . . by the internal Air'. On such lines, built double track at £7,000 a mile, 700 tons a day each way could be carried, and 'passengers may be conveyed to the greatest distance through the country with ease and safety at the rate of a mile a minute . . . at the expense of a farthing a mile', mails and goods at 1d per ton per mile. He ended by offering £50 shares.

The financial results must have been disappointing, for he turned to building a steam carriage which ran in 1819 and 1821. Then in 1827 a new pamphlet reverted to his earlier ideas, but with more elaboration.

He saw three ways of operating a pneumatic railway. In the first a round iron tube of 24 in diameter would be laid between the rails. This would have an opening 2 in wide underneath it, protected by deep flanges, and submerged in a trough of water. A piston driven along the tube by compressed air would then move a carriage carrying 12 passengers at 20 mph. Medhurst saw the snag that a trough of water must lie flat, and suggested a rise at intervals rather like a canal lock, up or down which the carriage would pass by its own velocity : he does not seem to have worried lest the piston would throw the water out of the trough.

His second choice was a road carriage running over a 2 ft square cast-iron tube. Half of the top would be cast-iron and fixed, the other half copper or wrought-iron, to lift up and shut back into a groove. Within the tube, a piston guided by wheels on all its sides, leathered all round so as 'lightly or barely to touch the sides of the tube', and with a valve to control its speed, would propel the carriage. This he saw as 20 ft long, but not more than 3 ft wide, and streamlined 'with a vertical edge before and behind . . . that it may pass through the air with the least resistance from the opposing winds, or the pacific atmosphere' at 60 mph, power being provided by steam engines 20 miles apart. The cost was to be £12,000 a mile, for double track, including the steam engines.

But Medhurst clearly preferred his third alternative, a goods truck running inside a tube, and attached to a passenger carriage outside, both moving together and driven by very low pressure compressed air. He saw the whole of the top of the rectangular tube or 'canal' as a lifting plate of copper or wrought iron, hinged at one side, and lying close and air-tight on a cast-iron rail on the other. To 'make the plate shut down air-tight upon the cast-iron rail, without being riveted to it, there should be a groove all along, upon the top and inner edge of the cast-iron rail, and a thin edge of iron riveted to the plates all along, to fall into the groove; then if the groove is partially filled with some soft and yielding substance, as cork, wood, leather, hemp etc., the thin iron edge will bed itself into it, and shut so close that the air will not escape, with so light a pressure as 1 pound per square inch. The plate may be lifted up . . . and, when let down again, the edge will fall into the groove, by the spring and weight of the plate'.

The truck running on rails inside the tube would have an iron wheel to lift the plate two inches or so for about 8 or 10 ft. A bar of iron, fixed to the inside truck, would pass through this opening and be attached to the outside carriage by a chain or strap, so pulling it along on its rails, which should lie alongside the tube. The piston, with a valve in it to reduce the speed, would lie behind the truck, while ahead the air would be pushed out of the open end of the tube.

Steam engines of 185 hp, each with three pumps, were to be placed every twenty miles. At the same distance were to be stations, where the truck would come out into the open before entering the next length of tube. He preferred double track lines, but if not, 'when the carriage is to go through the canal, from the engine, the air must be forced into the canal behind it; but, when it is to go the contrary way, the same engine is to draw the air out of the canal, and rarify the air before the carriage, that the atmospheric air may press into the canal behind the carriage, and drive it the contrary way'; it would, he thought, take his engine and pumps 15 to 20 minutes to pump out the 20 mile tube.

'I have long paid my adoration to this aëriel and invisible deity. . . .', he wrote, offering his ideas as 'the pure effulgence of an untaught mind, and of limited talents'. His adoration had not been blind, for he had foreseen the later successful use of pneumatic tubes for postal and many other purposes. He had also visualised railways operated on the Rammell system, being propelled by atmospheric pressure in one direction and compressed air in the other, and had foreseen and attempted to solve actual problems of operation. He died in September of this same year 1827, and was buried at his native Shoreham.

Medhurst's work was overlapped by that of John Vallance, who took out a patent in 1824, and wrote three relevant pamphlets. The first of these, on *Facility of Intercourse*, issued in 1824, was prefaced by an entry from an imaginary dictionary of 1924, which puts us at once in sympathy with the author: 'Impossible : a word formerly much in use, even among persons of intelligence, but which is now considered to indicate paucity of information, limitation of intellect, and the absence of all grandeur of conception'. He worked along similar lines to Medhurst's proposals of 1812, suggesting iron tubes at first $11\frac{1}{2}$ ft in diameter, and then down to 6 ft, within which trucks fitted with a backboard almost the same size as the tube would carry passengers or goods, being propelled along rails by very low atmospheric pressure; he seems to have thought in terms of 2 in of vacuum.

He also invented a telegraph for his tube, utilising a moving column of water.

He lived at 1 Devonshire Place, Brighton, where he built a tube of wooden boards made airtight with canvas covering. It was nearly 8 ft in diameter and 150 ft long. Rails were laid inside it, and a carriage 22 ft long and 5 ft 6 in wide running on them was steadied with lateral wheels. Power was provided by air-pumps driven by a small and also a large steam-engine, and propelled twenty or more of his intrepid visitors in the carriage through the tube at about 2 mph in about 50 seconds. During 1826 and 1827 it was tried by a sprinkling of the peerage, including the Earl of Egremont, always interested in new inventions, members of Parliament, and the inhabitants of Brighton. It was the first atmospheric railway.

In 1826 the Russian embassy had it examined by Sir William Couling, a major of engineers in their service. His report considered a speed of 100 mph practicable and suggested a line should speedily be built 'from St Petersburgh to Tsarsko-selo, the River Volga, Moscow, and the Black Sea'. In his own Brighton, a town's meeting in June 1827 decided that Vallance's method 'either as it relates to the transit of goods from Shoreham Harbour, or to the conveyance of passengers between Brighton and the Metropolis, is entitled to the most cordial support of the Town'. He estimated a Brighton–Shoreham tube, between five and six miles long, at £75,000, envisaging a 10 per cent profit, and the London, Brighton & Shoreham Pneumatic Conveyance Company was formed, for the carriage of coal and bulky merchandise by his new method. But by 1828 Vallance had run out of money without finding a patron. 'Had it been my good fortune to have met with one candid examinant of influence', he says sadly, 'I had been spared years of trouble and anxiety'.

John Hague coincides in time with Vallance and Medhurst, for in 1827 he patented a system by which a partial vacuum was maintained in a tube by air-pumps, and the tube then connected to the cylinders of an engine, the pistons of which would then be moved by air pressure. This system found a real though limited application in powering cranes—some at Whitstable and London Bridge station are known—and also machine tools and tilt hammers. A similar system was designed by William Murdock; on a small scale lathes were being driven by it at Boulton & Watt's works at Soho about 1810, and it was later enlarged. In 1836 also, coal waggons were being hauled up an inclined plane out of Hyde Lane colliery near Manchester by atmospheric power.

Hague is memorable also for his apprentices. One of them was Frederick Bramwell, later Sir Frederick, who between 1846 and 1850 worked on a scheme for a tube railway between Hyde Park and the Bank on Vallance's system, trains fitting the tunnel closely being propelled by atmospheric pressure through a tube partially exhausted of air. More importantly, another of his apprentices was Jacob Samuda.

In 1834 came an English patent by an intriguing and almost unknown character, an American living in London, Henry Pinkus, who claimed to have been at work on atmospheric propulsion since 1825, when he had proposed it for canal traction, and who had a working model at premises in Wigmore Street. In February 1835 he issued a prospectus for the National Pneumatic Railway Association with a proposed capital of £200,000, in £20 shares with a deposit of £3, a copy of which was sent to I. K. Brunel and filed by him. Pinkus proposed to lay down single-track atmospheric railways along the country's principal roads; these would have a very large tube of 30 to 40 in diameter, with which the trains' running rails would be integral. These were flangeless, as were the running wheels, the carriages being steadied by horizontal wheels running on the sides of the tube— a suggestion developed by Prosser into his similar system of wheels placed sideways against a central rail to guide a train of flangeless-wheeled carriages along flat rails.

At this time Pinkus was proposing stationary engines every $2\frac{1}{2}$ miles, a big tube separated into sections by valves, a piston (this seems to have been a disc without packing) of large area (some 9 sq ft) supported on a rail laid along the bottom of the tube, and a low degree of exhaustion; he calculated that 2 in of vacuum would produce a tractive effort of half a ton, which he considered was enough to move a 100-ton train. He therefore envisaged only a small amount of leakage from his valve. This was a cord which fitted the slot of the tube. Instead of being pushed up from below, however, it was lifted from above by a 'governor' fastened to the carriage, and then pressed back again. This cord, 'elastic, flexible', was surrounded with a coat of felt and smeared over with 'unctuous matter' to keep it soft and effectively airtight; fixed above it was a series of iron plates, jointed so that they could rise and fall as the cord was lifted and then pressed back, which formed the top of the valve.

His prospectus was supported by letters from Michael Faraday, who had seen Pinkus's experiments, and Dr Dionysius Lardner, the scientific railway pundit of the day. Among the system's advantages, said the prospectus, were power to overcome gradients, a construction cost lower by one-third than conventional railways, low expenses of operation and maintenance, and the fact that existing railways (or canals) could use it. For railway conversion, he proposed a 28 in tube, and for canals, one of 22 in laid along the towpath.

By the end of 1836 Pinkus had been deterred from his large tube by the rising cost of iron, and had developed a new idea along John Hague's lines. He now proposed small tubes of about 10 in diameter stiffened by circular fins outside, about 15 ft long, with the ends socketed into one another, and exhausted by engines placed every five miles.

His valve was no longer a cord; instead, the bottom edge of a long, thin, polished metal sheet, 20 ft long by 5 in wide, was fastened to each side of the 2 in slot, the sheets being so curved that their top edges pressed together. Each was overlapped to the next and then riveted or soldered to it. 'The valve is formed into such vertical curves as that when screwed down, the upper edges forming the polished lips are pressed together by the flexure or spring of the metal, with a pressure of less than 1 lb per square inch of surface in contact, and when so fixed will always continue in the same state and form an airtight joint, unless forcibly separated'. Stops were provided to prevent the valve opening too far.

The expansion chamber of an atmospheric-powered locomotive was then connected to the tube through a hollow tongue moving along the valve, this chamber being in turn connected to the locomotive's cylinders. Atmospheric pressure drove the piston down, the air being then exhausted through the expansion chamber to the tube and so away to the air-pumps of the engine-house. The resulting vacuum enabled the piston, once more driven by atmospheric pressure, to make its next stroke. It was probably a model of this pneumatic locomotive, and not of the earlier large tube, that Charles Vignoles records he saw with George Stephenson. Vignoles thought it impractical; George said: 'It won't do'. The model was built by Messrs Johnston of Cursitor Street, and tried at Lord's cricket ground. In 1840, in his *Prospectus of a New Agrarian System*, Pinkus hopefully suggested ploughing by atmospheric power, using a steam engine and fixed underground main tubes connected to a drum of rubber hose carried on a similar pneumatic locomotive pulling an 8 or 10-share plough.

Then followed the curious incident of the elusive railway. In the autumn of 1832 the committee of the Kensington Canal, which ran inland from the Thames to the south side of Kensington High Street near Olympia, were thinking of extending their line either by a canal or a railway to join the Grand Junction Canal and the proposed London & Birmingham Railway, then before Parliament. John Vallance, now able once again to pay his printers' bills, which would have been much lower if only he could have kept to the point, wrote *A Letter to the Kensington Canal Company*, to suggest that they laid down a tube line instead, but from the London & Birmingham by way of Kensington basin to Hyde Park Corner to tap the West End traffic. No action followed, and when a railway extension of the canal was again suggested, it was by a separate company, the Birmingham, Bristol & Thames Junction, later the West London, which in February 1836 made a provisional agreement to buy the canal, obtained its Act in June, and completed the purchase in mid-1839.

Vallance was followed by Pinkus, who probably got the canal company's agreement to build an experimental line on the banks of the canal for his pneumatic locomotive. During the autumn and winter of 1836 he seems indeed to have laid some track (half a mile was proposed) fitted with 15 ft lengths of $13\frac{1}{2}$ in tube, and set up a 30 hp steam engine and three air-pumps. Seemingly he then hoped to float a West End Railway, using his system and Vallance's suggested route onwards to Hyde Park Corner. But if he had an agreement, it was with the canal committee, and he and his apparatus were removed by the new railway company. As he was to put it later, 'the . . . works were at the threshold of demonstration . . . when they were broken up . . . by the Directors of a public Company, against the will of the share-holders, with a view to violate a contract and avoid the payment of the purchase money of the patents'. No more was heard of it.

In 1839 another inventor, Christopher Nickels, took out a patent for a compressed air railway which need not detain us, for meanwhile a more important patent had been obtained.

On 3 January 1838 Clegg and the Samudas patented 'a new improvement in valves, and the combination of them with machinery'. The patent (No. 7920) suggested the use of a hinge of leather, plated with iron, the lower plate convex to fit the circular tube, sealing composition (Clegg first thought of tallow), and a heater, so providing what seemed like a practical solution to the problem of keeping an atmospheric tube reasonably free from leaks; otherwise the principle was Pinkus's, and through him, Medhurst's. Not to be outdone, on 3 August Pinkus filed another patent almost identical with that of Clegg and the Samudas, except that he suggested using a galvanic wire instead of a heater.

Samuel Clegg was born in Manchester in 1781, and was given a scientific training by Dr Dalton. He was apprenticed to Boulton & Watt, became interested in the work Murdock was doing there in using gas for lighting, and became a prominent gas engineer

—indeed, a principal creator of the new industry. Then, disastrously, he joined a firm of engineers at Liverpool, and lost all he had. He made a fresh start working as an engineer for the Portuguese government, and then, returning to England, became interested in railway works. The combination of his gas engineering knowledge and his railway interests probably led him to the idea which made possible the building of an atmospheric railway.

Jacob and his younger brother Joseph Samuda were sons of an East and West India merchant, Abraham Samuda, and his wife Joy d'Aguilar, Joseph being born in 1813. Jacob was a brilliant engineer, Joseph more of an organiser. In 1832 they became partners, and for ten years were mainly engaged in developing marine engines at works at Blackwall; in 1843 they began shipbuilding. Clegg and the Samudas met and interested each other, and together they made the first experiments, though the younger Samudas quickly became the active partners. The patent rights were put in the hands of trustees, to be used for the benefit of the patentees.

Clegg seems to have carried out his first tests in France, at Chaillot, in 1838, with the help of James Bonfil, presumably a Frenchman, who is said himself to have set up his own model of Clegg's system in M. Nilhus's factory at Le Havre. Early in 1839 he lectured on atmospheric railways to the French Academy of Sciences, which set up a commission to study it that included the well-known scientist M. Arago. Mr Herapath, of the *Railway Magazine*, commented sourly but correctly that Clegg's railway was 'in principle precisely Pinkus's, with the bare difference, as far as we can see, of the band [valve] being fastened down one side'. It was perhaps because Herapath thought Clegg had appropriated so many of Pinkus's ideas that he first began his attacks on the invention.

John Herapath, now rising forty, was a character. A Bristol man, he had been a mathematics tutor, and when thirty had engaged in a brisk controversy with the Royal Society. Becoming connected with railways, in 1836 he turned journalist as manager and part proprietor of the *Railway Magazine*, starting a new series. Then as sole owner, he converted it in 1839 to *Herapath's Railway & Commercial Journal*, which he and his son Edwin John ran for many years as a highly successful weekly. Herapath was bellicose, opinionated, outspoken, and unfair; he was also well-informed, with a nose for news and sympathy for the underdog, a detective of extravagant claims and unsupported statements, and a very competent mathematician and physicist, who in 1847 published a two-volume book of good quality, *Mathematical Physics*. His paper therefore never lacked readers.

From this time, *Herapath's Journal* continually attacked both the scientific basis of atmospheric propulsion, the operational claims made for it, and Samuda's estimated costs for constructing and working atmospheric railways. He maddened those who were promoting and those who wanted to be fair to the new invention, by his offensive and exaggerated journalism. Clegg, Samuda, Brunel, Cubitt, must have loathed him, and not the least because in the end he turned out to be right.

Clegg reacted to Herapath's initial attack by failing to invite him to an experiment with a model set up at the Samudas' ironworks at Southwark. This drew two men weighing 18 stone in a carriage weighing 160 lb up a 1 in 10 incline 180 ft long at 7 mph, using a tube of $3\frac{5}{8}$ in diameter exhausted by a steam engine, and 8 in of vacuum. Before that, 30 ft of the same tube had been laid level and pumped out by four men. It had then been altered to 102 ft at 1 in 30, to be altered yet again for public tests. Herapath presumed his exclusion was because Clegg had 'exhibited his piratical propensities on Pinkus . . . and probably thought the editor was not so easily humbugged in these matters as certain titled folks may be'. At this point the Samudas probably decided to improve their public relations, by asking Herapath to a special demonstration. He then admitted that the model worked well, but added, shrewdly enough, that, assuming the valve could be kept sound, uninfluenced by the weather, and free from wear, the expense of the tube and its maintenance, 'countless fixed engines and all their concomitants, raising their smoky heads every two miles, and constantly kept going, are no dwarfs to set against the locomotive and the extra expense of cuttings and embankments'. All the same, he added, atmospheric travel would be much more comfortable than the 'ceaseless noise and nuisance of locomotives as now constructed'.

A pamphlet, *Clegg's Patent Atmospheric Railway*, was now published to explain and make known the system. Given what railway engineers of 1839 had experienced of the cost of railway construction and of locomotive performance, it must have sounded most attractive. Against an estimated £42,000 a mile for building steam lines and providing them with locomotives, Clegg's railway offered £10,456 a mile, and for working costs £1,246 against £4,141 a mile per annum to convey 1,400 tons a day. Valve repairs he put in at £50 a mile per annum, and coal for stationary engines at £62. Less cutting and embanking, promoters were told; lighter rails, and away with high locomotive maintenance costs and fuel consumption, both increasing with faster speeds.

In June 1839 Clegg and the Samudas, after abortive negotiations with the London & Greenwich, sent Bonfil to approach the board of the partly-built Birmingham, Bristol & Thames Junction Railway, which has already figured curiously in our story. This was to run from the London & Birmingham at Willesden under the Grand Junction Canal, across the Great Western main line on the level, and past Wormwood Scrubs to the Kensington canal basin. Agreement was soon reached whereby the patentees would lay down $1\frac{1}{4}$ to $1\frac{1}{2}$ miles of line, roughly from the Great Western Railway to Holland Park Avenue, supplying rails, apparatus, and ballast, and have occupation for eight months from the date of agreement. If the experiment succeeded, the railway company were to have the use of the patent free in exchange for repayment of the patentees' expenses; they contemplated using it from a temporary station at Shepherd's Bush to their junction with the London & Birmingham. If it did not, the apparatus was to be removed eight days after notice had been given.

In fact, the Samudas complained in 1840 that they had only

been able to take possession of about half a mile of embankment on gradients of 1 in 115 and 1 in 120, the rest being unfit for ballasting. The experimental section ran from just south of the Great Western line alongside Wormwood Scrubs to the Dalgarno Gardens bridge, the engine-house being on the Scrubs side of the line just north of Scrubs Lane bridge. They laid old rails from the Liverpool & Manchester Railway and a 9 in diameter tube, and provided a 16 hp steam engine and an air-pump with a $37\frac{1}{2}$ in diameter cylinder.

The first test took place on 11 June 1840, the second on the 15th. On the first few days of testing, at vacuums between 16 and 23 in, and using the piston carriage alone or with one coach, the greatest speed attained was 36 mph, weight moved $11\frac{1}{2}$ tons, and number of passengers carried, 75. The Samuda brothers, asked by the *Railway Times* for a report, wrote that they saw the advantage of atmospheric traction as absence of unavailable weight to be hauled compared with locomotives, and of the weight and friction of the rope compared with rope haulage; safety, since collisions were impossible; speed, dependent on the vacuum attained; ability to work steep gradients; and the cheapness of fixed engines compared with locomotives. Finally, they repeated the cost figures they had given in *Clegg's Patent Atmospheric Railway*.

On 29 June the *Railway Times* man himself saw the experiments, and wrote: 'we have no hesitation in now bearing our personal testimony to the perfect efficiency of the system—though what its merits in an economical point of view may be, we are not yet fully prepared to say'. On the same day, with Prince Albert present, a speed of 40 mph was reached with the piston carriage only.

Prospects looked good, the vacuum obtained improved as the composition became embedded in the groove and the valve fitted better, and in August the railway journals carried advertisements for the Atmospheric Railway Company, to be incorporated by Act of Parliament with a capital of £400,000, and Clegg and Jacob Samuda as engineers. Its objects were to grant licences

III. (above) An atmospheric train ready to leave Kingstown for Dalkey; (right) the same scene in 1955, before the station was rebuilt; (below) a local street name

slí na ōτρɑen
ATMOSPHERIC RD.

IV. *The engine-house at Dalkey, with its supply pond in the foreground and Kingstown in the distance; (below) Dalkey, looking north from Barnhill bridge; the site of the atmospheric railway terminus was to the right of the train*

and to contract with railway companies for haulage of their traffic, but giving them an option to buy the carrying rights. The *Railway Times* thought this willingness to contract for haulage removed 'every difficulty in the way of success . . . excepting . . . such as may rise from the conflict of private interests, or from the reluctance of innovation common to all established bodies'. In another pamphlet, *Clegg and Samuda's Atmospheric Railway*, the 1839 figures were revised and elaborated. As these were maintained for many years, they are worth noting :

		£ Per Mile
Estimated cost of construction		
locomotive lines		37,600
Atmospheric lines		
Track	8,500	
Tube and apparatus	5,200	
Fixed engines, air-pumps and engine-		
houses	1,400	
Pistons	20	
		15,120
saving		22,480
Estimated annual working expenses including interest,		
locomotive lines		4,130
Atmospheric lines		
5 per cent interest on £15,120 ...	756	
Maintenance of track and valve ...	300	
Wear and tear of fixed engines ...	70	
Coal	214	
Wages : engine-men and firemen ...	60	
train conductors	26	
Renewal of travelling apparatus and		
composition, sundries	200	
		1,626
saving		2,504

Leaving the track aside, the estimated cost of installing atmospheric apparatus was given as £6,620 per mile. This figure can be compared with the actual cost (see page 172) of £21,700 per mile on the South Devon.

c

The Samudas now wanted a real railway upon which to demonstrate the value of their system, and one was to hand. The London & Croydon had been authorised on 12 June 1835 from what is now West Croydon for $8\frac{3}{4}$ miles to Corbett's Lane to join the London & Greenwich, whence the company had running powers to a separate station at London Bridge. Engineered by William Cubitt, the line had been opened formally on 1 June 1839, the public service beginning on the 5th.

At Jolly Sailor, now Norwood Junction, a mile from West Croydon, the London & Brighton Railway, authorised in 1837, with running powers over both the London & Greenwich and the London & Croydon, left Croydon metals; it was to be opened in September 1841. All three companies' rails could also be used by the South Eastern Railway's line to Dover, authorised in 1836 and opened throughout in 1844. This branched from the London & Brighton at what was then Earlswood Common and is now Redhill.

In mid-1840 the London & Croydon were having trouble in getting their locomotives to cope efficiently with the 1 in 100 bank between New Cross and Dartmouth Arms (Forest Hill), a bank that was soon to be shared with London & Brighton and South Eastern long-distance trains. So, on 4 August, Samuda Bros. wrote to W. A. Wilkinson, chairman of the London & Croydon, suggesting that if atmospheric working were adopted on the bank, the annual cost would be £2,711 instead of the current £5,490. They went on to propose that, without interrupting traffic, they should provide atmospheric traction on the bank at their own expense, to pull 60 ton trains every 15 minutes at 30 mph and then contract for hauling all the company's trains at 20 per cent per ton per mile cheaper than current costs. The company were to be empowered to buy the right to haul their trains atmospherically at £1,000 plus the cost of installation— cheap at the price, assuming the system had by then been successfully demonstrated. Ten days later they added that nothing would prevent the Brighton company using locomotives if 'they should from caprice prefer doing so'.

The company asked the opinion of William Cubitt, their own engineer, and J. U. Rastrick of the London & Brighton. Then, having had their comments, they wrote back asking 'how you propose to meet the difficulties suggested, in getting the invention on the line, and whether you are prepared to submit to stipulations in the first instance for its removal and the restoration of the line whether it succeeds or not should such measure be found expedient to the company?' It was a question expecting the answer 'no', and the correspondence ended.

However, the Wormwood Scrubs tests went on every Monday and Thursday from 3 to 5 p.m., the public being allowed for about a year to ride in the trains, but they died out of the news, and it seems likely that they would have ended without having attracted serious interest if support had not come from across the Irish Sea, where there was a man not reluctant to test an innovation.

CHAPTER THREE

1842-1844

THE building of a new harbour at Dunleary (the anglicised form of Dun Laoghaire), a few miles south of Dublin, had been begun by the elder Rennie in 1817, after he had reported that it was impossible to improve that of the capital. Dunleary's name was changed to Kingstown after the visit of George IV to Ireland in 1821.

The Dublin & Kingstown Railway was authorised by an Act of 1831, James Pim of a Dublin banking family being one of the chief promoters and becoming treasurer. George Stephenson and Joseph Locke were consulted, the former made an estimate, Alexander Nimmo was appointed engineer, and the Irish Board of Public Works agreed to a provisional advance of £75,000. Nimmo died in January 1832, and the Board then asked their own engineer, John Killaly, to make a report. He did so, and on it the directors decided to proceed, appointing Charles Vignoles engineer at £800 p.a. 'thus superseding my old friend Stephenson, which is itself worth a thousand more', as Vignoles wrote in his diary.

The line was built on the 4 ft 8½ in gauge by William Dargan the contractor. It was opened on 17 December 1834 to a temporary station at the western pier of Kingstown harbour; this first railway in Ireland was 5½ miles long, and in 1837 was extended for half a mile to a terminus near the packet wharf. By this time Vignoles and Pim had become firm friends—which was to be important later.

The line was immediately successful, though previously the commercial world of Dublin had had little faith in it, and a flourishing commuter business was built upon frequent services, low fares, the issue of family and season tickets, and 'second and third-class vehicles . . . much superior to those employed upon any English railway', in the opinion of the *Railway Times*. In its first eight years it carried about ten million passengers. Dividends were never less than 5 per cent, and were to rise nearly to ten.

The Commissioners in charge of the new harbour works had built a double-track tramroad to carry granite to Kingstown from the quarries at Dalkey. In 1833 the railway company introduced a bill to extend their line past the harbour to Dalkey, the quarries to be linked to it by a branch and the tramroad closed, but lost it. In 1838, by which time one tramroad track was enough to take the stone traffic, it occurred to James Pim that the second might be used for a horse-drawn railway extension of the Dublin & Kingstown to Dalkey, and he started talks with the Board of Public Works.

Then the Wormwood Scrubs tests were held. Vignoles was one of the first to attend, and soon became a convert. In turn, he interested Pim, whose concern in Irish railways and canals extended more widely than the Dublin & Kingstown; he was, for instance, a considerable shareholder in the Grand Canal. It seemed to Pim that, should the atmospheric system prove practical, it might provide Ireland with low-cost railways, and so strengthen the Irish economy. He therefore sent Barry D. Gibbons, the engineer of Kingstown harbour, and Thomas F. Bergin, the Dublin & Kingstown's secretary, to see the tests, and suggested to Clegg and the Samudas that the Commissioners might be willing to use their line for an extended experiment; if so, the Dublin & Kingstown would help. Clegg and Jacob Samuda therefore approached the Treasury, who side-stepped any active part in testing the new invention, but agreed that one track of the tramroad could be made available.

While this application was being considered, a distinguished group attended the Wormwood Scrubs tests on 16 July 1841, after they had been running for a year without apparent result in terms of action. They included James Pim, Mr McMullen of

the Grand Canal, Vignoles, Macneill the engineer, Johnson of
the Forth & Clyde Canal, Baxendale, chairman of the ambitious
South Eastern Railway, and Lord Morpeth, who was especially
concerned with Irish railways. 'The interest taken in the day's
proceedings by Lord Morpeth and many of the above-mentioned
gentlemen', said the *Railway Times*, 'arose from the probability
that this invention will be put to the proof on the tramway from
Kingstown to the village of Dalkey, with a view to its adoption
on an extended scale in the projected Irish railways.'

The conditions of the test were demanding. The track and
tube had been roughly laid fourteen months before, 'and in their
present state on the ground,' said the *Railway Times*, 'present a
kind of zig-zag caricature of a railway; certainly no locomotive
engine would venture over them.' It probably seemed to Pim
that a system which would enable trains to run at 25 mph under
these conditions would indeed provide Ireland with cheap railways.

He decided to back the invention himself, and in so doing to
seek Government support for its wider use. Therefore in December, after Samuda had met the Dublin & Kingstown board,
the Treasury received an application to borrow £25,000 from
the Commissioners of Public Works, on mortgage of the Dublin
& Kingstown, to build the Dalkey extension. Pim also wrote and
published two pamphlets. In *A Letter to the Right Hon Lord
Viscount Morpeth* he argued that single-track light railways,
built with natural curves, low bridges and the minimum of engineering works, were what Ireland needed. Such lines might well
be atmospheric. As Government permission was needed to build
a line to Dalkey, he suggested that a trial should be made 'under
the superintendence of the Board of Public Works for Ireland'.
Later, if successful, the railway could be turned over to the
Dublin & Kingstown. The second, *A Letter to the . . . President
of the Board of Trade*, asked that the Government should itself
investigate and report on the atmospheric system. The patentees,
he said, would gladly put the test track at Wormwood Scrubs
and their drawings at the investigators' disposal. Accompanying

plates showed how greatly the system's use could lessen railway engineering works.

The Government agreed, and in March 1842 Lt.-Col. Sir Frederick Smith of the Royal Engineers and Professor Barlow* made their report, which was published as a Parliamentary paper. They concluded *(a)* that the principle of atmospheric propulsion had been established, and that economy of working increased with the length and diameter of the tube; *(b)* that an atmospheric line would cost much more to build than one for locomotives, because the expense of the tube and stationary engines would outweigh savings on construction; *(c)* operating costs would be less if trains were frequent, but upon maintenance costs of, e.g., valve and pistons, nothing could be said without fuller experience; *(d)* safety was equal to rope-operated railways, but there seemed to be 'some practical difficulties in regard to junctions, crossings, sidings, and stoppages at road stations, which may make this system of less general application.' The writers added for Pim's benefit that 'the atmospheric principle seems well suited for such a line as the projected Kingstown & Dalkey is represented to be.' The editor of the *Railway Times* commented : 'We do not think that these results promise much for the general adoption of the atmospheric plan of propulsion.'

The report was, however, good enough for Pim, encouraged by Vignoles and firmly supported by Bergin. On 6 April a special meeting of the Dublin & Kingstown agreed to use the atmospheric system on a $1\frac{3}{4}$ mile extension to Dalkey. The cost exclusive of locomotive power was estimated at £12,000, and the Samudas had agreed to install an engine, all atmospheric apparatus, and an electric telegraph for £11,000 more, of which £2,500 would remain in the company's hands until the system worked satisfactorily, this being defined as ability to draw 26 tons gross on an incline of 1 in 120 at 30 mph. In addition the

---

* Tests at Wormwood Scrubs seem to have stopped in the summer of 1841, and to have started again early in 1842, presumably for Smith and Barlow's benefit. These produced speeds up to 40 mph with loads of 5 tons. They finally ended in March 1843, when the plant was removed and the site returned.

company might install it on their Dublin line without payment of royalty, and would receive a percentage of the Samudas' income from all licences to use the system in the British Isles. The cost of the extension ought not therefore to exceed £25,000, which the Commissioners of Public Works in August agreed to lend.

The proprietors had hoped for a growth of commuter and pleasure traffic at Dalkey, and reckoned that if the extension paid its working expenses, then the increased revenue it brought to the Dublin line would cover repayment charges. Pim considered that 'the additional sum which would be received by the Company from the "curious", who would be desirous to witness so wonderful an experiment as a railway upon an atmospheric principle, and for that purpose would travel . . . would more than pay the entire amount of the risk which the Company would run in the undertaking'. At worst, if the new system were a complete failure, the loss would not exceed £5,500.

The *Railway Times*, which in 1840 had attacked 'reluctance of innovation', was horrified: 'Why should a serious risk be incurred, for the attainment of what at best *must* be a very inconsiderable benefit, and which *may* turn out to be wholly illusory . . . until further inquiry has been made . . . it were madness to build upon the calculations and conclusions of parties so deeply interested . . . as the patentees'. However, the Dalkey went ahead. Meanwhile in June further very satisfactory tests were held at Wormwood Scrubs, at which, apart from engineers, 'a very large number of the first City capitalists' attended and speeds of 40 mph were reached, and Brunel, just back from looking for a line to link Genoa and Milan, was understood to be thinking of using atmospheric power for a mountain section with gradients up to 1 in 30, the air-pumps to be worked by water power. In that month also Vignoles read a paper on the system to the British Association at Manchester, the Prussian Government were interested for a hilly section of line in the Rhenish provinces, and Sir Marc Brunel thought the principle would come in useful for the lifts of the Thames Tunnel.

In July a second edition of Pim's *Letter* appeared, and in reviewing it the *Railway Times* began to climb back on the bandwagon. Thanks largely to Pim, it said, the atmospheric system 'occupies a very different position from that which it held some eighteen months ago . . . the hundreds of well-qualified judges who *then*, from not having personally examined into its merits, deemed the "Atmospheric Railway" a something in which fraud and folly struggled for the mastery, *now* look upon it as one of the most important inventions of the age'. Representatives from the London & Croydon Railway and the Thames Tunnel attended tests, and now Pinkus tried to assert his claim to be the system's real inventor, only to be battered by the simultaneous weight of Vignoles, Clegg, and Jacob Samuda, though throughout the period that atmospheric lines were working he persevered in asserting his claims and threatening the companies that were using Clegg's and the Samudas' system.

No Act was needed for the Dalkey extension, as it was to be built on the tramroad site, but it had to use the same sharp curves and to be sunk below ground level to avoid level crossings. Vignoles was engaged as engineer and William Dargan contracted for the earthworks and masonry, the company to lay rails. In September Samuda Bros' contract with the Dublin & Kingstown was signed, and was followed on the 26th by the formal taking possession, 'sod and twig', of the land from the Board of Public Works. The great experiment was about to be made on a commercial railway, and little happened meanwhile, though tests continued at the Scrubs, among others for French, Hanoverian, Spanish and Württemburger engineers, and Vignoles lectured to the Royal Cornwall Polytechnic Society, when the *Railway Times* reported that 'we believe the Cornwall people are becoming sensible of it, and various lines in Great Britain could adopt it with advantage—from Chester to Holyhead, for instance'. One of the visitors had been M. Teisserenc de Bort of the French department of Ponts et Chaussées, sent at the request of the French ambassador, who had himself seen an earlier test. Teisserenc reported favourably to the Minister of Public

Works, and initiated French governmental interest in the system.

Meanwhile a controversy had arisen at Kingstown, a group of inhabitants demanding that the atmospheric line should be covered over where it passed in front of the harbour, the company objecting to covering more than a short section on the grounds of expense and the danger that trains, running downhill by gravity from Dalkey, might because of wind resistance fail to reach the station, but stop in the proposed tunnel. James Walker, President of the Institution of Civil Engineers, agreed to arbitrate, and decided that rather more should be covered in than the directors had proposed. This was agreed to, and the covering was done with heavy cast-iron plates, openings at intervals being protected by wrought-iron railings.

The time of waiting for the Dalkey to open was enlivened by the publication at the turn of the year 1843 of an attack on the conclusions of Sir Frederick Smith and Professor Barlow by Thomas Bergin, who had a convert's enthusiasm. He pointed out that the Dublin & Kingstown had been the first public body to take the initiative in introducing railways to Ireland. Subsequently the Irish Railway Commission had been appointed, ` and had made recommendations without result. So the Dublin & Kingstown had again stepped forward with a new system of propulsion that promised cheap construction, speed, and safety, the first especially necessary if Ireland were to have a railway system, and which had the secondary advantage that the stationary engines might be able to burn peat, and be used also for such agricultural purposes as powering flour mills. He then launched into a well-argued attack on the Report's technical findings.

The *Railway Times* supported him, now attacking Smith and Barlow; these in turn replied to Bergin, and a brisk engineering controversy followed which kept interest alive, especially as the two authors of the *Report* had to admit error. Cubitt was stated to be a convert; in April James Thompson read a paper on atmospheric propulsion to the Glasgow Philosophical Society, and said that while 'he did not wish to be understood as prepared to advocate its superiority, in all circumstances, over the existing system of locomotive engines . . . he was convinced that it contained the elements of certain success, if properly worked out and judiciously applied'; Scott Russell was reported more favourable than formerly, considering the question now a purely practical one: Could all the details be made to work efficiently, durably, and economically?

In May talk of an atmospheric line along the banks of the Grand Canal from Dublin to Portumna and Ballinasloe filled the columns of the *Galway Vindicator*, and in June a less ambitious scheme was brought forward for a passenger line from the capital along the same canal to Sallins or Naas. The engineering line-up was now thought by the *Railway Times* to be: Vignoles entirely in favour; Brunel, Macneill, and Rendel 'speak respectfully and rather favourably of the invention and agree that it deserves the trial'; Cubitt has 'written strongly in favour of the present trial': but Robert Stephenson, Locke, Bidder, and Rastrick 'are generally understood to treat the proposition with the utmost contempt'.

On 17 August 1843 the tube was exhausted for the first time, on the 18th a train was run, and then at last the moment came for the first public trial of the Dalkey line; as the tunnel into Kingstown station was unfinished, this was to start at Glasthule bridge. Everyone was anxious to see what would happen, not least the men who had built it, 'as the whole affair had been a perfect riddle to them, solved in every variety of way, some the most ludicrous'.

On Saturday 19 August large placards were put up to warn the 'immense crowds assembled along the line', and a cordon of police stood in readiness. The crowd was perhaps divided into those who said 'It can never be made to go', and those who replied 'It can never be got to stop'. First the valves were tested. Then at 5 p.m. the scientific guests arrived, 'the signal was given by men stationed with small flags along the line, and the piston carriage, with two passenger carriages, one second and one third class, attached, moved along *per se* amid the joyous shouts of those assembled. It seemed more as if some magic power were at work, some force that no human energy could waken into existence. . . . Mr Joseph Samuda was on the piston carriage, and several gentlemen took guests in the other carriages, and they describe the motion as more than ordinarily smooth and easy.' A maximum of 28 mph was reached. In the evening Clegg and the Samudas entertained the scientific and other visitors. James Pim was there, the Lord Mayor of Dublin, the Chairman of the Irish Board of Public Works, and the editor of the *Allgemeine Zeitung*. After dinner Joseph Samuda announced that the directors of the Grand Canal had invited him to investigate the proposed line from Dublin to Sallins.

It all seemed wonderful, not least because the first practical atmospheric railway had been laid not in Britain but in Ireland. The *Dublin Evening Mail*, praising Pim and the directors of the Dublin & Kingstown, wrote : 'this wonderful and extraordinary development . . . of a power the existence of which was questioned, and its applicability to practical purposes either denied or sneered at. Doubtless this experiment . . . will produce a revolution in the whole system of railway construction and traffic, and in the end be universally adopted.' By the end of September daily trials were being held, and speeds of 60 mph were rumoured. By October 'the Atmospheric is quite the "lion" of the place. . . . It is rumoured that the principle is to be applied without delay to the Box tunnel on the Great Western Railway.'

Though the Dalkey's opening was delayed by the tunnel at Kingstown, the trials were attended by many of the eminent. In November Brunel was there; so was Major-General Pasley, the Inspector-General of Railways, who told the Board of Trade the system was perfectly efficient and safe, and M. Mallet, Inspector-General of the Public Works in France, sent by the Minister after M. Teisserenc's earlier report. More rumours put the maximum speed up to 80 mph.

General Pasley reported on 15 November that the line worked

well: 'the real question of superiority between the atmospheric railway and former systems will therefore be a question of expense'. For instance, Samuda thought that the engines could be five miles apart instead of three. However, when the proposed extension of the Dalkey to Bray was built, it would be seen 'whether this sort of railway is more economical'. In December it was said that the King of the French was strongly in favour of establishing the system, and that estimates had been made for an atmospheric line from Margate to Ramsgate.

Early in January 1844 the first English prospectus appeared, for the Gravesend, Rochester & Chatham Railway, with Brunel as engineer.

Though the estimates provided for locomotive power, it said that the committee and engineer recommended the use of atmospheric 'both as a means of keeping the capital within a very moderate compass, and increasing the profits by a reduced charge of working'. Its use was possible for a line through Cornwall, there was talk of its application to a railway from Berlin to Charlottenburg and others in Württemberg, and the Dalkey, running free trips while waiting to open, had had visits from engineers from Belgium and Bavaria.

And now the Prime Minister, Sir Robert Peel, spoke on the subject in Parliament. Much later, after the South Devon had failed, Herapath was to blame Peel for having so much contributed to raising men's expectations. In a debate on railways on 5 February, he was reported as saying: 'At this present moment, a new discovery in science was in practical operation, and it would be well for the existing railway companies to consider well what might be the effect of the Atmospheric Pressure System. Scientific men, who had gone in doubt to examine the practical working of that system, had come back with very altered opinions as to the utility of applying the principle to railways. He had seen the ingenious men who were entitled to the credit of the discovery, two brothers of the Jewish persuasion; and from all he heard, the experience of its working on a few miles of road was such, that he thought a doubt might very reasonably be entertained whether it was not capable to being equally applied to hundreds or thousands of miles'.

Just before the speech, the Samudas had suggested atmospheric traction to the committee of the proposed Chester & Holyhead Railway, who approved the principle, but referred its applicability to their engineer, Robert Stephenson. He went over to Dalkey, and came back to report against it, accompanied by a mass of experimental data that was later published, and formed a quarry in which those looking for arguments against the system dug happily. The care with which Stephenson had experimented, and the precision with which the report was written, gave it great influence with engineers just at a time when Peel was exciting the imagination of promoters and investors: indeed, no engineer of importance was converted to support of atmospheric traction after it had appeared. It warned that the cost of maintaining the valve was yet unknown, and concluded that the system was not an economical method of transmitting power, being inferior in that respect both to locomotives and to stationary engines using rope haulage. However, it could be useful on some short railways where traffic was heavy, where frequent, fast trains of moderate weight were needed, and where gradients were too steep for locomotives.

Rope traction by stationary engines was widely used at this time to work steep sections of line; for instance, from Camden down to Euston station on the London & Birmingham, or Cowlairs to Queen Street, Glasgow, on the Edinburgh & Glasgow. On the $3\frac{1}{2}$ mile long London & Blackwall it worked a commuter service. Therefore engineers naturally thought of the atmospheric with its stationary engines as a variant of rope haulage—Stephenson called it a rope of air—as well as an alternative to the locomotive, and in his report he included comparisons between rope and atmospheric haulage based on tests made on Camden incline. P. W. Barlow later carried out others on the rope-worked Tyler Hill incline of the Canterbury & Whitstable.

In March the Gravesend, Rochester & Chatham was refused leave to proceed in Parliament, as the notices given to landowners had not distinguished between two different plans, for an atmospheric and a locomotive line. Pim, with others of the Dublin & Kingstown company's directors and shareholders, was supporting it, and he petitioned for leave to bring in a late bill on the grounds that Brunel was the first to propose using the atmospheric system on a line long enough to develop its advantages, and had chosen the Gravesend, Rochester & Chatham because, so the *Railway Times* reported, it 'presents a singular combination of advantages for trying such an experiment—it is just of sufficient length—the country presents considerable difficulties —the probable traffic over it would be enormous—and the experiment being tried in the neighbourhood of London, would insure to it the fullest and most impartial examination, and all may be completed within twelve months'. But the House did not make an exception of the bill. The Thames & Medway Canal company then utilised its Strood tunnel to build the single-track Gravesend & Rochester Railway, which was opened on 10 February 1845 and soon afterwards bought by the South Eastern.

About the end of February M. Mallet's report had been published in France. It gave details of the experiments he had made on the Dalkey line, went into such problems as operating long lines, mixing passenger and goods traffic, passing trains, and working steep inclines, and compared costs of construction and operation. It was highly favourable to the new system and ended by strongly recommending the French government to choose a line where atmospheric traction could be tried. One of Mallet's remarks has special charm : 'I am aware that in France time has not the value it possesses in England, but the very use of rapid means of transit will teach us to appreciate it.' Herapath was less impressed by Mallet's report : 'an eminent instance of the incompetence of mere engineers to judge of mixed practical and scientific questions. Very few of his "facts" are true, and not one of his deductions correct'.

Regular running to timetable began on the Dalkey on 18 February, passengers being carried free.

Then, in March 1844, an advertisement appeared:

ATMOSPHERIC RAILWAY
KINGSTOWN AND DALKEY
NOTICE

THIS Railway will be opened for PUBLIC TRAFFIC on Friday NEXT, the 29th instant.

The Trains will start from KINGSTOWN every HOUR and every HALF HOUR, from Eight A.M. till Six P.M., and from DALKEY every QUARTER and THREE Quarters after the Hour from a Quarter-past Eight A.M. till a Quarter-past Six P.M.

FARES

Second Class .... Threepence

Third Class .... Twopence

As yet there are not any First Class Coaches.

By Order.

T. F. BERGIN

The extension had cost £39,000. The great experiment had begun.

We must now return to the London & Croydon, over whose double track between Corbett's Lane and Jolly Sailor, and up the long incline from New Cross, were now running not only its own suburban carriages, but the long-distance trains of the London & Brighton and the South Eastern. Even without taking into account the congestion on the London & Greenwich between London Bridge and Corbett's Lane, it was a situation in which punctuality was difficult, and the operation of a fast, frequent suburban service to Croydon impossible.

The London & Croydon, wanting to improve its commuter service, and the South Eastern, building its Dover line, both felt it essential to get access to London free of the congestion of the Greenwich tracks and the toll of 4½d a passenger levied by that concern. So in the session of 1842–3 the two companies sought an Act to build a line 1¾ miles long from the Croydon just short of the Greenwich junction at Corbett's Lane to Swan Street, near

v. *(above) The cutting of the Dalkey atmospheric line at Castlepark Road, though the bridge dates from 1854-6. The little building on the right is connected with the original tramroad; (below) Curve just north of Sandycove station. The walling above the grass bank dates from the atmospheric railway*

VI. *(above) A piston carriage on the Croydon line. The driver is screwing down the brake; behind him a gauge shows the vacuum; the lever in front probably works a valve in the piston acting as an emergency brake; (below) the wooden viaduct at Norwood carrying the atmospheric line over those to Brighton and Dover. On the viaduct a signalman stands outside his shelter*

the 'Bricklayers' Arms' in the Old Kent Road, and to build a station there. The London & Greenwich naturally opposed, but the Act was passed on 4 July 1843. It provided that the Croydon should pay one-third and the South Eastern two-thirds of the cost of construction and maintenance, and gave the latter powers to buy the Croydon's share on giving six month's notice; these were used in 1845.

Knowing that pressure would soon be eased by the new line, the London & Croydon, at a by no means crowded shareholders' meeting in December 1843, decided to extend their own railway for 8½ miles to Epsom at an estimated cost of £180,000, this being the Croydon's reply to a branch from Kingston to Epsom projected by the London & South Western.

The London & Croydon realised that their proposed extension would be more expensive to build than the LSW's branch, but reckoned that it would bring additional traffic to their own tracks now that they were about to provide a better service at lower fares, and to improve accommodation by closing in the second class carriages and roofing the thirds. On 1 May 1844 the line to Bricklayers' Arms opened, and the Croydon then put on an hourly service to it, additional to the trains they were already running to London Bridge, at strikingly lower fares—1s second-class against 1s 9d. In June their chairman was able to report to the shareholders that 'There have been during the month of May since the Bricklayers line was opened, about six times as many passengers to and from the Bricklayers' Arms Station as there have been to and from the London Bridge Station, and the receipts have been about three times as great between Brick-layers' Arms and Croydon as between London Bridge and Croydon.'

Soon after the bill for Brunel's atmospheric Gravesend, Rochester & Chatham had been introduced, the Croydon company offered to join the South Eastern in building a line from their own railway to Chatham. The latter first agreed and then declined. Thereupon the Croydon decided to support the scheme by themselves. About the same time, William Cubitt, who had

D

built the Croydon, suggested to W. A. Wilkinson, its chairman, that the Epsom extension, if continued into London by a third track alongside the existing Croydon metals, would provide an excellent means of testing how efficiently atmospheric traction might provide the answer to commuters' needs. From which it was a natural development that the London & Chatham proposal should also be seen as an atmospheric line to join Brunel's (with a branch to the LSW at Esher, it became the London & Chatham and Chatham & Portsmouth Junction, with a capital of £1 million and also with Brunel as engineer), and that Wilkinson should quickly have come to see his company as pioneers both of long-distance and suburban atmospheric traction, and himself as the man who would revolutionise railway operation.

At the shareholders' meeting on 7 March he told his flock that 'if the atmospheric principle were adopted on the long line,* as it was meant to be adopted by Mr Brunel on the other, he had no doubt that the passage from Chatham to London might be accomplished in an hour and a half, thus enabling the railway to compete successfully with the river'. He went on that 'he was convinced that ultimately the atmospheric system must supersede that now in use, and looking forward to this, he thought the Croydon Company were in a peculiarly favourable position'. From which it was only a step to explaining how valuable it would be on a new separate track of the Croydon line itself, in overcoming the bank between New Cross and Forest Hill, in enabling a train to be dispatched every five minutes with no possibility of collision (very important were the Croydon line to gain Epsom and Chatham traffic also) and in leaving the existing Croydon tracks free for Brighton and Dover long-distance trains. He ended by emphasising that Cubitt was as cautious as he was able, and the resolution to build a London & Croydon atmospheric line was carried with only one dissentient. Support for the Chatham extension was less enthusiastic, twelve being in favour and eight against. The *Railway Times* was not enthusiastic, saying of Wilkinson: 'He will end by finding that he has caused

* The line to Chatham.

the Company to lay down a costly apparatus of 20 miles in length, when an addition to the stock of three locomotives would have performed the work.'

This kite-flying having been successful with the shareholders, the Board agreed on 1 April that the Croydon & Epsom should be built by a nominally separate company as a single-track atmospheric line with double-width bridges, and continued by an atmospheric third track laid alongside the existing lines all the way to London Bridge or Bricklayers' Arms. Samuda was there, and held out the prospect of a reduction of a half to two-thirds in working expenses compared with a locomotive line. A fortnight later the talk was of trains every 15 minutes in each direction, with a non-stop timing of 22 minutes from Epsom. The Board preferred London Bridge to Bricklayers' Arms as their terminus, and therefore suggested a take-over to the London & Greenwich, who refused. They in turn replied that they would lay the atmospheric line only to Bricklayers' Arms, unless the London & Greenwich would part with their existing south line, in which case they would run solely to London Bridge. They got another refusal, and then wrote to the South Eastern to ask permission to build the atmospheric line to Bricklayers' Arms. Meanwhile the Board of Trade, to whom the L & C had notified their ideas, had replied that while Mr Gladstone* could not pledge himself in advance of a bill, 'he is aware of the importance of an early and complete trial of the atmospheric system on an extensive scale, and will be prepared to support such a desirable object by any means not inconsistent with principle and Parliamentary usage'.

Cubitt, Samuda, Brunel, and Robert Stephenson met in May before the Parliamentary committee on the Croydon & Epsom. Cubitt was cautious: 'I am not prepared to say that atmospheric railways would be best for general purposes on all railways, but there are particular situations, such as in this case, where it can be of advantage, besides testing the value of a discovery founded on sound philosophical principles.' Brunel spoke of running faster

---

* Then aged 34, and President of the Board of Trade in the Conservative Government of Sir Robert Peel.

trains more often, trains that could cope with gradients and would be cheaper to run. Jacob Samuda, the *Railway Times* handsomely admitted, 'has gained for himself the laurels of being one of the most clear-headed and intelligent witnesses ever examined on a scientific subject before a Committee of the House of Commons'; and Robert Stephenson emphasised the system's operating disadvantages of inflexibility, being wholly governed by the size of the tube and the power of the stationary engines, inability to reverse a train, put it into a siding, or cope with an accident, but on comparatively weak ground when arguing against a purely suburban line.

In June the bill was through the Commons, Cubitt was favouring an extension beyond Epsom to the LSW at Thames Ditton or Esher, and the prospectus of the London & Chatham and Chatham & Portsmouth Junction atmospheric line, with branches to Gravesend and Dartford, was out. Atmospheric exaggeration was deflated by a humorist in the *Railway Times*, who wrote that his broker had recommended Croydon & Epsom shares, 'for the Chairman had recommended a plan to work that line on the atmospheric principle, without any cost!'

The Croydon shareholders' meeting of 26 June had much to consider, for the ideas of their board were growing—'They regarded the Epsom as being necessary to the Croydon, and the Chatham as necessary to the Epsom.' The chairman claimed that both Parliament and the Board of Trade wanted a fair trial made of the atmospheric system, and that their adoption of it had helped their bill against that of the LSW, though it added that the Epsom line would be so graded that locomotives could use it if necessary. 'I am of the opinion (supposing the atmospheric plan to answer)', he said, 'that although it might in the first instance cost something considerably more than the mere making an extension locomotive line from Croydon to Epsom, by, say £120,000 or thereabouts, still the difference of expenditure between working the fixed installation and locomotive power, together with the advantages of increased traffic attendant upon working the line upon the true short-traffic principle, viz. frequent trains, high velocity and low fares, will, I hope, both repay and justify the additional outlay, to which may also be fairly added something . . . as due to the novelty . . . and which alone if successful will, in my opinion, pay the whole extra cost before it be worn off.' In preparation for their atmospheric lines, Cubitt, Wilkinson, and three other directors went to see the Dalkey line in July, 'which', says their minute book, 'they found in every respect to answer their most sanguine expectations'.

By the autumn traffic on the Croydon line was booming. The company had been authorised to build the Epsom extension and also their own atmospheric third track, and they had asked Cubitt to make a preliminary survey for a direct atmospheric line to Portsmouth, which would give a better route from their railway than via the proposed Chatham line's branch to the LSW at Esher, and that company's branch from Bishopstoke (Eastleigh) to Gosport. By the turn of the year these schemes had grown further. The proposed London & Chatham and Chatham & Portsmouth Junction was now extended to join the Canterbury, Margate & Ramsgate Railway near Chilham; another line was proposed from the London & Croydon to Tonbridge, Maidstone, and on to the South Eastern at Ashford, together with an extension of the Croydon & Epsom to Dorking (unless this were provided by the Direct London & Portsmouth), and a branch to Orpington. All were to be atmospheric. The Direct London & Portsmouth now became a separate company to build an atmospheric line from Epsom to Portsmouth at a cost of £1¼ million, with Cubitt's assurance that it was unnecessary also to provide for locomotive working. A special meeting of the Croydon shareholders approved all these, and also powers to double their own atmospheric line in the future. The little Croydon frog was indeed puffing itself very big.

The provisional committee of the DLP first met in September. The chairman was W. A. Wilkinson. Hananel de Castro, one of the atmospheric patent trustees, was there, and so was J. L. Ricardo, MP, much interested in things atmospheric. The engineers were William and Joseph Cubitt. The allotment of shares was completed during the month, and Cubitt suggested a branch to the South Eastern Railway at Dorking and then by Reigate to Redhill, with another from it to Guildford, and was asked to survey them. A bill was prepared, and in November agreement was reached with the atmospheric trustees to pay £500 a mile to use the patent, payment to be made as the line was built.

Meanwhile, back in May Jacob Samuda had read a paper on atmospheric railways to the Institution of Civil Engineers, with William Cubitt in the chair, and the *Railway Times*, considering there was a case for the principle on the Epsom line, was fascinated by his struggle with the locomotive's supporters. 'Many . . . have worked themselves into a pitch of affection for the locomotive, being justly proud and excited with delight at its wonderful achievements; and now to witness the prospect of its extermination!'

In June this journal, with the confrontation in mind, set out the opposing arguments in a long editorial:

Clegg and Samuda say

    (a) that the loss of power due to locomotives having to pull their own weight can be avoided;

    (b) that the weight of rails and chairs can be lessened by one-third;

    (c) that the wear and tear of locomotives, as opposed to stationary engines, is as 18 to 1;

    (d) that the full power of a stationary engine is always available, and that it can burn coal, at half the price of coke; [Coke was then normally used for locomotives.]

    (e) that the original cost of construction of an atmospheric line is much less, because only a single track is needed, and greater gradients can be allowed;

    (f) stationary engines cost less than locomotives to run.

Robert Stephenson says

    (a) the atmospheric system does not transmit power economically; in this respect it is inferior both to locomotives and to stationary engines using ropes;

    (b) no greater speed is possible than with locomotives;

(c) atmospheric lines will seldom be more economical to build, and often they will be more expensive;

(d) the atmospheric principle might, however, be applicable to a few short lines.

The paper concluded that the new system should have 'a further and more extended trial', and a week later printed a letter from Clegg saying that the appeal is now to experience: 'Let anyone examine the hourly working on the Dalkey Railway; let him inquire of the Directors of that Company what has been hitherto the results of their experience, whether the anticipations held out to them by the patentees have been disappointed? Whether in any one point they are dissatisfied, or repent their adoption of the system?'

Later in the month, however, Sir John Macneill wrote for the board of the Dublin & Cashel Railway a report condemning atmospheric traction second only in influence to Robert Stephenson's. Before that James Pim had promoted his Grand Canal Atmospheric line along the canal banks to Sallins, but when the Dublin & Cashel seemed likely to supplant it, he tried to persuade that company to adopt atmospheric traction, and involved himself in a brisk controversy with the Cashel's chairman, Peter Purcell, one that ended with Macneill's report.

In July the papers reported that the French Government had agreed to experiments with the system. Then, on 28 August, at the first shareholders' meeting of the South Devon Railway, after Samuda had suggested to the board the advantages of the atmospheric's cheap construction costs and ability to overcome gradients upon such a line as they proposed to build, and a visit to Dalkey in early August by a South Devon party which included the chairman, Thomas Gill, the board supported Brunel's recommendation to build the line as a single-track atmospheric railway, 52 miles long between Exeter and Plymouth. The shareholders agreed. To the Samudas it must have seemed the triumph of all they had worked for.

In September a party of Great Western, South Devon, and South Wales Railways directors and engineers, including Lord

Courtenay, Charles Russell, Daniel Gooch, and Brunel, again went to Ireland. There they met Jacob Samuda, and spent time examining the Dalkey. A Dublin paper saw in this visit a plan for an atmospheric line connecting Waterford, Wicklow, and Wexford with Kingstown and Dublin; a service of powerful steam-boats between Wexford and Fishguard; and an atmospheric line thence through South Wales to join the Great Western, which could be expected to share the Irish traffic with the route by way of Liverpool and the Grand Junction Railway.

In the north, another atmospheric project had sprung up and put in a bill; the Northumberland in competition with the Newcastle & Berwick, also with a bill, to build a line between those towns as part of an east coast route to Scotland. Lord Howick was chairman, W. A. Wilkinson vice-chairman, H. de Castro and J. L. Ricardo on the board, and Brunel engineer. The evidence given on the Croydon & Epsom bill was cited to show the soundness of atmospheric traction, which would mean fewer earthworks and a faster and safer line. There was plenty of cheap coal locally for the stationary engines which, suggested the prospectus, could also be used for other purposes. Abroad, the Italian & Austrian Railway was publicised, 185 miles from Verona to Ancona, with Brunel as engineer. The line was described as suitable for atmospheric traction, but the writer said that before expenditure was incurred, its applicability to a long line would have been tested on the Croydon & Epsom.

In all this there was much to encourage those who supported air against steam. But the year ended badly, for on 12 November Jacob Samuda died, killed by the giving way of an expansion joint of the engine of the *Gipsy Queen*, one of the first vessels to be built by Samuda Bros. His was the best brain and the finest mechanical engineering ability behind the atmospheric system, and if he had lived, it is just conceivable that the story might have ended differently.

CHAPTER FOUR

1845: THE RAILWAY MANIA

THE bills for the Direct London & Portsmouth, the various Croydon extensions, and the Northumberland Railway had been sent first to the Railway Department of the Board of Trade for their observations. In January they reported against the Portsmouth, and Samuda wrote off to Pim on the 15th: 'I am sorry to tell you the mandate of the Board of Trade is against us for the Portsmouth line. We however must not expect to get everything. It will be some compensation if, taking the "vested interest" point of view (which they appear to do) they give the Croydon the permission to make the Tonbridge and thus secure them the Dover tolls which would be lost if the Dover Co. succeed in their project to that place. I begin to tremble for the Northumberland.' However, the Portsmouth's shareholders agreed that in spite of the adverse report they would promote their bill in Parliament, provided that the deposits of those who wanted to withdraw would be refunded. Thereupon the London & Croydon company agreed to repay such deposits and take over the shares—as it turned out, some three-fifths of the allotment.

In mid-February, the Board commented on the Kent lines. The London, Chatham & Chilham was especially criticised for gradients more severe than those ever proposed for a locomotive line, having 15 of its first 30 miles at 1 in 50. The Board went on, referring to atmospheric traction, 'If that system had already been applied successfully upon any long line of Railway, the severity of the gradients . . . would not have been considered so objectionable. It is clearly, however, impossible for us to assume the success of the system, as to which so much difference of opinion exists among Railway Engineers, and which has not hitherto afforded such proofs of its merits as could warrant us in giving preference to projected undertakings, the success of which must depend upon results, as yet uncertain, while other projects are offered, to which no such uncertainty applies.' This was good news for the rival projects of the South Eastern and the North Kent promoters, and did not augur well for the atmospheric bills in Parliament.

A few days later the Board reported on the Northumberland project, saying the mechanical problem had been solved on the Dalkey, and that atmospheric traction would probably succeed also on a longer line: the Croydon & Epsom would show. 'It is impossible,' they said, 'not to feel the highest interest in the progress of an experiment, whose success hitherto has been sufficient to induce eminent authorities to entertain strong hopes that the result may be an acceleration of speed in travelling, combined with the general introduction of a system of very frequent trains and low fares.' But success could not yet be assumed, 'not merely as a mechanical theory, or as applicable under peculiar circumstances, but in a practical and commercial point of view, as applicable to railways generally'; they presciently added that for longer lines they thought that double tracks might well be required, and that they were doubtful whether atmospheric traction could be applied to mixed traffic, and especially to heavy mineral trains.

Unless something could be done to counteract this flow of Civil Service common sense, it seemed likely that no further progress would be made in getting long atmospheric lines through Parliament until the Croydon & Epsom or the South Devon had proved itself. And that was a long way ahead for impatient inventors and patentees. A few days after the Board's report on the Northumberland Railway, Joseph Samuda and Samuel Clegg petitioned Parliament for the appointment of a Select Committee to inquire into the merits of the atmospheric system of railway, and to hear the evidence of engineers and other persons on the subject. Action quickly followed, and on 14 March a committee was appointed.

Meanwhile, the Railway Department had produced some more pertinent remarks. Less than ten years before, a gradient of 1 in 105 was considered impossibly difficult for locomotives, and we have earlier noted the troubles the London & Croydon had in 1840 with their bank of 1 in 100 at New Cross. Indeed, one of the attractions of atmospheric power had been its suggested ability to surmount steep gradients. But now, on a proposal to use atmospheric traction on inclines of 1 in 60 on each side of the summit of the proposed Leeds & West Riding Railway, the Department commented that gradients of up to 1 in 50 were quite acceptable for locomotives, and, exceptionally, even those up to 1 in 37½, like the Lickey incline, were usable by heavy trains helped by a special type of banking engine. Writing of Cornwall and Devon, they showed uncertainty of the South Devon even at this early date : 'As the South Devon Railway is not yet completed, and it is not yet certain whether the Atmospheric or Locomotive system may be ultimately used upon it'; and of the approaches to London, they suggested postponement of schemes for lines from Epsom to Dorking or Dorking to Reigate until the results of the Croydon and Epsom experiment were seen. If atmospheric traction were successful, then 'it would seem better suited than the locomotive system of traction to the nature of this section of country', and an Epsom–Dorking line might be built. Otherwise, one from Dorking to Reigate might be preferable.

The Select Committee reported on 22 April : the evidence given before it is the most complete of the confrontations of the time, and its conclusions represent the high-water mark of the atmospheric achievement. Of the more important witnesses, Samuda, Brunel, Vignoles, and Cubitt favoured atmospheric traction; Robert Stephenson, Locke, and Bidder did not. To represent what experience existed came B. D. Gibbons, engineer of the Dublin & Kingstown, and T. F. Bergin, its secretary.

One is especially struck by Brunel, who seems to have gone out of his way to give an unconvincing display which yet succeeded in convincing. Asked what were his reasons for recommending atmospheric traction on the South Devon, he started his answer with 'I will try to recollect them'. Then:

Q. 'I suppose you have set out in your own mind the manner in which the whole of that line is to be constructed?'

A. 'To a certain extent, but not entirely. The whole system of working a line with atmospheric apparatus requires a great deal of consideration, and requires many new contrivances . . . and I do not think that I have at all completed yet, to my own satisfaction, all the details of these arrangements. I think I see my way clearly to effect them, but I should hope still to effect many improvements.'

When, after Samuda's explanation of how atmospheric pressure could be used to check trains on steep descents, Brunel was asked: 'What mechanical means do you contemplate adopting in the descending of steep gradients', he replied: 'I have not yet determined; sufficient for the day is the evil thereof, and it does not occur in the first twenty miles.'

On some points he and Samuda contradicted each other, Samuda stating as definite decisions matters, such as the installation of water tanks to exhaust the tube as well as engines, which Brunel treated as still matters for consideration. Certainly Brunel gives the impression that he resented Samuda's inventor's attitude, and this caused him to give an unfortunate answer following upon a disastrous admission. For, asked about the rate of possible leakage from the train tube, he replied that it would probably be about the same as at Dalkey, but 'I do not pretend to have made any of these calculations with precision, or any attempt at precision, for I do not feel that I have enough data to do it'.

The Committee pressed him:

Q. 'You know that Mr Samuda calculated the leakage of the pipe as 5 horse power per mile?'

A. 'Yes, I recollect that.'

Q. 'Do you allow as much as that?'

A. 'I really cannot say.'

Finally, 'Do you contemplate any source of irregularity on the atmospheric system?'

'I do not foresee any; there will of course occur some, but I do not know of any general cause operating that is likely to produce irregularity.'

He was to find out the answers the hard way.

Barry Gibbons and Thomas Bergin described the Dalkey at work. Gibbons, asked about the effect of frost, said that although the leather had been hardened, it had not been affected 'to an extent to interfere with its use', though he amended this later to explain that when cold weather had come on suddenly at the end of November, he had had loss of vacuum on four days till the men had got along the whole line with their composition. Bergin was more confident. He attributed the frost trouble to the use of a wrong composition—beeswax, and hard Russian tallow, instead of beeswax and lard oil (olein, solidifying at $-6°C$) that Samuda had specified, and said that after he had had the wrong mixture taken out and replaced, there had been no further trouble. The leather remained soft even in frost, and the composition 'from frequent working . . . acquires a degree of tenacity which I never saw in any other waxen composition before, and adheres with great force both to the leather and the iron'. Maintenance men, however, had a small supply of composition to replace any pieces that broke away.

Charles Vignoles had recommended the atmospheric system for the Dalkey line, and at the time of the Select Committee regarded himself as its leading exponent: 'I was the first engineer who recommended its adoption at all in a practical way, and the result has every day confirmed the impression that was then made on my mind.' In lines of his then before Parliament, however, the question had been left open, since gradients could be altered later by permission of the Board of Trade. This was done because: 'a great number of directors and persons connected with those railways have not that confidence in the atmospheric system which I have; in fact, I may say that I am somewhat in advance of the companies and the public generally upon that point'. He was realist enough, however, to realise that the public could only be convinced by successful operation on a line more important than the Dalkey. For himself, 'I am not prepared to recommend it indiscriminately; but I am quite prepared to say that, under most circumstances, the atmospheric would be preferable to the locomotive.'

Vignoles had become interested in the system from the first exhibition of the model in Paris. He spent a good deal of time at Wormwood Scrubs, and was very impressed by seeing the test line brought back into use after some weeks of idleness, when the track had become uneven, and the piston had had to push ice and snow out of the tube which 'was like the back of a sea serpent', though the joints were sound. It was this experience that led him to recommend it for the Dalkey line.

'The great principle of the atmospheric system,' he said, 'is the substitution of an economical stationary power for an expensive locomotive power'; therefore trains could run frequently, cheaply, fast, and safely. For long lines he thought a single atmospheric line would do the work of a double locomotive line; methods of passing and overtaking had been worked out, and 'we only want experience to teach us in what particular detailed manner we are to overcome difficulties in the mode of working'. He saw atmospheric operation as being especially useful where gradients were steep and traffic likely to be heavy—as on the Blackburn and Bolton line. Where traffic was sparse, as in Ireland (he instanced the Waterford and Limerick line), he thought reservoir-water could drive the pumps, and steam engines could be used also for purposes such as milling.

Robert Stephenson was impressive, for more than any other engineer who gave evidence, he understood how a railway was run. Of single-line atmospheric working as equivalent to double-line locomotive railway: 'the thing is physically impossible . . . the application of the atmospheric system implies the utmost conceivable regularity in the velocity from end to end of the line, in order that the meeting of the train may take place at the same time, under all conditions of weather'. Whereas on a double locomotive line an irregularity only affects one train, on a single track atmospheric it affects all. Again, he saw the problems of junctions. It was for this reason, the impossibility of making a junction except at a break in the tube, that he rejected the system for the proposed Dudley and Stourbridge line.

He was led to conclude that, operationally, the atmospheric system was only suitable for light, frequent, non-stop trains on commuter lines—the exact conditions that obtained on the Dalkey. 'On short lines . . . where the traffic is very large, and where the departures of trains are very numerous, the atmospheric would be an exceedingly convenient arrangement, but not more economical than the Blackwall, and not so convenient as the Blackwall where you have intermediate traffic to accommodate.'

Stephenson had one great technical objection. 'The proportion between the power necessary to work the pump and the proportion of that power applied to the train gets worse and worse as you go on increasing your vacuum.' Was Brunel to remember those words on the South Devon? Heavy trains meant high vacuum readings—therefore the system was only suitable for light trains operating at low readings. 'The valve . . . is the prominent imperfection of the system, however beautifully in theory it may be overcome.' Yet there was nothing mechanically wrong with it, and no means in sight to improve it.

It was impressive evidence.

The sixty-year-old William Cubitt, building the London & Croydon and recommending atmospheric extensions to Epsom and Ashford, was less so. He saw that the method was especially attractive for lines in very hilly districts, or where heavy passenger traffic required to move at short intervals in large numbers very quickly, as on his own Croydon, yet added that with experience and good management it would probably be possible on long lines and for goods trains; he saw that single-line atmospheric working would not really allow expresses to be run, only to add that the London & Birmingham could be worked single-line by such power. And he ended: 'I am fearful of going too

great a stride at a time; I wish to proceed, as experience may
enable me, gradually . . . I am anxious to see everything tried,
and tried fairly.'

Joseph Locke's views were similar to Stephenson's. Clegg &
Samuda had solved the mechanical problem, but not the operational. Anything going wrong on an atmospheric railway would
affect everything. And how could night mail trains be worked
except at high cost? And how could coal branch lines be brought
in, except at crossing stations? He pointed out, too, that engine
speeds were capable of being much increased, and that the electric
telegraph would make single-line locomotive working safer. G. P.
Bidder said much the same. Ideas of single-line atmospheric
working on the London & Birmingham were just too perfect in
theory; in practice they were impossible—there would be too
many stoppages.

And then Samuda came confidently back to encourage the
committee. The design of the valve had been improved: for
lightly used lines the tube would be exhausted by water reservoirs, fed by a very small steam engine. But the system was
really most useful in heavy traffic, working more trains at a
higher speed, with goods trains run at night. And think—no
noise, no dirt, safety, comfort, and identity of interest between
management and public in frequent fast trains at low fares.

And so the committee reported. Of the Dalkey, with its nineteen months of working behind it, that it operates 'with regularity and safety throughout all the vicissitudes of temperature,
and that the few interruptions which have occurred have arisen
rather from the inexperience of the attendants, than from any
mechanical defect of the system'. They liked the promise of
safety: there had been fourteen collisions and thirteen accidents
to locomotives during the last fifteen months; they liked the in-
ducement to railway management to run frequent cheap trains,
and so 'Your Committee think that there is ample evidence
which would justify the adoption of an atmospheric line at the
present time . . . experience can alone determine under what
circumstances of traffic or of country the preference to either

VII. *The engine-house at Croydon (above) then, and (below) as re-erected in 1851 as part of the waterworks*

VIII. *Forest Hill on the Croydon line (above) on the station side, and (below) on that of the engine-house*

system should be given.' And, the crucial statement for the atmospheric promoters; that a proposed atmospheric line should not be rejected in Parliament on the grounds that it is too steep for locomotives, or compared to other lines solely on grounds of suitability for locomotives.

As far as the committee were concerned, the atmospheric system could be regarded by the legislature as a real alternative to steam, and atmospheric lines could be authorised even if they could not also be used by locomotives. The way was clear for Samuda. The public was not so sure. One humorist in the *Railway Times*, who affected the Quaker style, thought two-way operation on a single track impractical—'who, in the name of nonsense, dost think would submit to be thus jerked across the country like a galvanised frog?'

Meanwhile the engineers had been arguing among themselves. In February, P. W. Barlow read a paper to the Institution of Civil Engineers. He had been asked to report on the usefulness of the system to the proposed Tunbridge Wells branch of the South Eastern, and, regarding it as a rope of air, had carried out experiments on the rope-worked Tyler Hill incline of the Canterbury & Whitstable Railway. He commented on the likely high installation and working costs, criticised the probable operational difficulties, using similar arguments to Robert Stephenson's, and concluded that the system was only applicable to fairly level high density passenger lines, or to those which could be worked one way by gravity. Sapiently, he thought the New Cross incline would be the Achilles heel of the Croydon experiment because of the increased tractive force that would be necessary, and did not think the system applicable to the South Devon.

He was most interesting, however, in his remarks on power loss, for he picked up the very high loss on atmospheric railways —much higher than on rope-worked—but thought it to be connected with air friction in the tube. 'It must be apparent,' he says, 'that the loss from leakage does not form a large proportion of the lost power, and there is therefore but little field for mechanical improvement.' Joseph Samuda, Pim, C. H. Gregory

E

the Croydon's engineer, Brunel, and Cubitt were all there; Robert Stephenson was not. All thought that the practical problems could be overcome. Thermodynamics was a subject of the future, and it was not then realised that certain power losses were inherent in the system. Probably thermodynamic losses were about 35 per cent of the power input; air friction lost another 10–15 per cent, leakages about the same, the mechanical losses at the piston brought the overall efficiency down to 25–30 per cent.

Not long afterwards, the Institution gave three more evenings to the topical atmospheric question, the debate being initiated by George Berkeley, who had once worked with Jacob Samuda, and had later been one of Robert Stephenson's investigators on the Dalkey when he was preparing his report for the board of the Chester & Holyhead. Berkeley's paper once more criticised the system for the practical operating difficulties it would create, and for its likely working costs. The subsequent discussion, initiated by Robert Stephenson and Joseph Samuda, was mostly concerned with the accuracy of Stephenson's observations and deductions, though Vignoles and others tried to get it back on a practical course.

Brunel and Cubitt did not take part, but G. P. Bidder drew attention to power loss due to air friction, and two mining engineers strongly supported him from their experience in mine ventilation. Compared to the February meeting, the weight of opinion had moved heavily against Samuda, who described himself as fighting the atmospheric battle single-handed, and being astonished at finding in the world not indifference, or doubt, but an active and energetic opposition 'which, if successful, would have had the effect of crushing the system before it had been developed or its capabilities ascertained'. However, the Croydon was building, and that would be 'sufficient to set the question at rest— he expected to exceed the performance of the Locomotive Engine —Mr Stephenson on the contrary expected the failure of the system. A short time would judge between them.'

While the Committee had been sitting, the great railway mania was getting under way; in March the pace was increasing, and by May it was at full speed. Its impact can be followed in such a magazine as the *Illustrated London News*. Atmospherically, occasional news paragraphs about tests on the Croydon line were supported by full pages with accompanying woodcuts, explaining Samuda's and Pilbrow's systems, and rounded off by more varied entertainment as the bubbles and the freaks began. There was the South London Suburban with Nathanial Briant as engineer and a capital of £800,000, to build a line partly on viaduct and partly on embankment from London Bridge to Camberwell, and thence by two branches, one to Mitcham and one towards Dulwich. Atmospheric traction, said the promoters, was 'admirably adapted to a line requiring a constant succession of trains', and was free from noise, smoke, and dust. There was D. D. Jameson's Hydro-Pneumatic Railway, whereby air, compressed hydraulically in lineside installations, was to add to the power of the piston in the atmospheric tube 'to preserve the great speed of the atmospheric railway, but to propel larger trains, on high gradients'. There was the Direct London & Manchester (called Remington's line to distinguish it from another scheme), with a capital of £3 million, and a length of $177\frac{1}{2}$ miles, which considered that 'as one line of rail will be sufficient for the larger portion of its course, a great saving of labour and materials will be obtained. There will be no tunnelling or extraordinary earthwords on the railway, as such are not necessary on a line worked on the atmospheric principle.' The promoters promised a $3\frac{1}{2}$ hour service between the two towns. To be in the fashion, the highly dubious Great Eastern & Western, from Great Yarmouth to Swansea, promised that they would use the new power if 'it should eventually prove advantageous to their undertaking', and later the most peculiar Great Welsh Railway, from Bangor via Shrewsbury, Hereford, Merthyr Tydfil, and Swansea to Pembroke, reserved the right to use atmospheric power on certain parts of the line, while protesting that the whole 'does not present any engineering difficulties of importance'.

There is special charm in a badly-printed four-page undated prospectus for Cooke's National Railway—'Broad Gauge, Guide-

Form of Application.

TO THE PROVISIONAL COMMITTEE OF THE

Wakefield. Ossett. And. Dewsbury. Direct. And. Atmospheric. Railway.

RAILWAY COMPANY.

Gentlemen,

I request that you will allot me   *55*   Shares of £ *10*
each in the above proposed RAILWAY, and I agree to accept that or any lesser number that
you may please to allot me, and I undertake to pay the Deposit of £ *7s. 1s.*   per Share on the
same, and to sign the Subscriber's Agreement, and the Parliamentary Contract when required.

Dated this   *25*   Day of *Oct.*   1845.

Name .... *Jonathan. Coates.*

Residence .... *Delphend. Pudsey*

Place of Business, (if any) *Cloth Manufacturer*

Trade or Profession ....

References .... *Mr. Abraham. Archer Junr.*
  Osset
  Cloth Manufacturer

An application for shares in an atmospheric railway

wheels, Atmospheric and Telegraph throughout'. With a capital
of no less than £40 millions, in £20 shares (£2 2s 0d deposit),
the managing director, William Robert Cooke (manager to the
late John Collinge, Engineer, Lambeth), was to build new lines
from London to Edinburgh, Exeter, Hull, Shrewsbury and
Gloucester with branches. Passengers were to be carried at 2d a

mile first class in saloons; at 1d second in glazed and cushioned carriages; and at ½d third in covered carriages. There is a touch of the true engineer in the statement: 'The direct line is adopted throughout and will be as closely as possible adhered to both for economy and dispatch, and while the mountainous land of Scotland, Wales and Cornwall is shunned, there will be some glorious engineering difficulties surmounted in the heart of England.' One feels that, even if Mr Cooke did not get his £40 millions, he had some very happy times making plans.

June brought many schemes for a central station in London to which all railway termini could be conveniently linked by rail or road; they flowered from the Report of the Metropolitan Improvements Commissioners in February 1844, which had recommended an embankment along the river from Blackfriars to Westminster Bridge and the building of new through roads to improve the movement of traffic. They were of all sorts: we are only concerned with the atmospheric projects.

One was the City of London Junction Railway, with a capital of £2¼ million to build a central station behind Moorgate Street for all the railways in London, and a new Thames bridge. Atmospheric power would be used to prevent inconvenience and noise, and 'one stationary engine on the Surrey side of the Thames, one at the central station, and one at Paddington, will be sufficient'. Another, the Thames Embankment & City Railroad Co, who proposed 'to embank the river from Hungerford market [Charing Cross] to Blackfriars bridge, forming, in the space recovered from the shallow parts of the stream, public gardens, terraces and docks, and along the edge of the embankment a double line of road; the outer portion as an atmospheric railway, the inner as a macadamised road for ordinary vehicles . . . at Blackfriars bridge . . . the proposed double road will leave the embankment, and be continued along a new street 66 ft wide leading to the Blackwall Railway, and Whitechapel . . . the railroad portion of the line will join the Blackwall at Fenchurch Street or the Minories, and be carried along the middle of the new street upon an open framework of iron girders, at the level of the first floor windows'. There were to be rail links with lines at Hungerford and Blackfriars bridges, and a chief City station near London Bridge. The description of the embankment, and the announcement that there would be a station every 500 yd for interchange between the atmospheric line and omnibuses, nearly foreshadows what actually came to be built, except that trams took the place of piston carriages.

In Ireland Pim's Grand Canal Atmospheric from Dublin to Sallins had grown to the Dublin & Galway Grand Canal & Railway, with Joseph Cubitt as engineer and William as consultant. The prospectus proposed that the new company should buy the Grand Canal and build their line along its banks. It would be atmospherically-worked, as the promoters 'look forward to the complete and entire mechanical success of the atmospheric system' after the decisive trial it would have on the London & Croydon and the South Devon. There would be frequent light trains, a 10 in tube, the electric telegraph, perhaps wooden rails to save expense, and maybe spare water power from the canal to help work the railway. Indeed, it would be possible to tow barges at night using the railway's tube, but otherwise, the committee conceded with a lapse into common sense, by giving them steam engines. Trains would take less than four hours for the journey, and 'to the citizens of Dublin the Highlands of Galway will be brought within the reach of a pic-nic party'.

In Ulster two Belfast attorneys, John and Alexander Montgomery, proposed an atmospheric line from the city, primarily to popularise the bathing facilities at Holywood on the shore of Belfast Lough. It got considerable local support, but was dropped after pressure from the Belfast & County Down Railway. There was also a brief proposal for a line from Newry to Castleblaney.

Now appeared advertisements for Pilbrow's Atmospheric Railway & Canal Propulsion Company, chairman, the Earl of Essex, engineers, Alexander Gordon and Frederick Braithwaite, with a capital of £600,000, who were willing to grant licences for the use of Pilbrow's patent. James Pilbrow had been born at Stratford, Essex, on 16 February 1813, and as an experimenter seems to have specialised in studying the effects of expanding steam upon varying surfaces.

His system did away with the tube valve. Instead, the top of his tube opened into a square pipe bolted to it. On each side of the interior of this pipe, about 30 ft apart, were pairs of spindles which passed through airtight collars to project above it. As the piston passed through the tube, a bar above and fixed to it passed between these spindles and turned them. Their projecting portions then engaged a rack beneath the piston carriage, forcing it forward. The public could see a working model on a scale of one inch to the foot at the Adelaide Gallery. One day they might even see a real line, for a Pilbrow railway was advertised from Milk River to Montego Bay, Jamaica, with a capital of £1 million, and Braithwaite and Pilbrow as engineers, and two were promoted at home, the Direct London & Gravesend, and the Direct London & Dublin, the latter from Birmingham via Shrewsbury to the Chester & Holyhead at Bangor. No valve, no difficulties about level crossings, no heater carriages, a stationary engine only every ten miles and therefore £3,000 a mile less in construction costs, and ability to vary the diameter of the tube were, the company claimed, its advantages. One would think overwhelming objections were the difficulty of keeping the spindle collars airtight, lubricated, and yet unobstructed under working conditions, and to prevent them breaking when hit by trains at high speed.

In August the *Mining Journal*, which had hitherto carried the sub-title *Railway and Commercial Gazette*, though little railway news, changed its name to the *Mining Journal and Atmospheric Railway Gazette* (it kept it until March 1847), and came out for the atmospheric, but rather in support of Pinkus and the inventors of freak systems than of Samuda. The scientifically-minded part of the public could also visit 'the Atmospheric Railway, Daily at Work, carrying Visitors, at the Royal Polytechnic Institution'. The enterprising Professor Bachhoffner was accustomed first to lecture on the principle, and then to give rides on the model, at 1s a time, schools half-price.

These were encouraging excitements, but meanwhile there were setbacks. Towards the end of June the bill for the Northumberland Railway failed. At the beginning of July the preamble of the Direct London & Portsmouth passed; the bill went through the Commons, and in early August the Lords. Then, on a technical disagreement between the two Houses on the rights of certain parties to be heard before the Lords committee, it was lost for the session. All the bills for the enlargement of the London & Croydon failed. The five-mile Bray extension of the Dalkey, promoted by the Kingstown & Bray, was rejected on standing orders because the wrong plans had been sent in and, in spite of Brunel's advocacy, Parliament stood back the South Devon's atmospheric branch to Tavistock for a year until the system should have proved itself on the main line.

In his evidence to the Commons committee on the Cornwall Railway, intended for atmospheric traction, Brunel had said that the associated companies supporting the line had insisted that it should be capable also of locomotive working, and that he and Captain Moorsom had observed this condition in laying it out. It would be safe for fast steam trains at 30 mph, and others at 22 mph, with higher speeds if atmospheric traction were used. Asked what size tube he recommended, Brunel said he would like more experience of the South Devon first, but thought 20 in would be necessary on the main line; that would be able to take 40 ton trains. However, Parliament judged that the curves would be too sharp and the gradients too steep, and did not like the steam train ferry proposed over the Hamoaze; therefore the bill was stood back for the line to be regraded so that locomotives would find it easier to work, and for a possible Hamoaze bridge. Thus many of the envisaged economies of atmospheric working were lost. Parliament had certainly not been encouraging.

Among lines already authorised, the contract to construct the Croydon & Epsom had only just been awarded, and orders given for the stationary engines. On the London & Croydon itself the first five miles between Dartmouth Arms (Forest Hill) and Croydon were not yet open, even for testing, because the stationary engines were not ready. Down in Devon tubes were being laid and engine-houses built on the first section of the South Devon between Exeter and Newton.

In July the *Railway Times* reported that 'in the northern share markets', especially in Liverpool and Leeds, 'a terrible mania has seized the operators'. 'Business in many of the new lines is rapidly falling off, parties of judgment fearing that ere long we shall experience a terrible crisis, brought on solely by the folly of desperate speculators buying at prices which no events can ever justify.' Caution began to creep into advertisements for atmospheric railways. Remington's line, now renamed the London & Manchester Direct Independent, acquired Sir John Rennie as engineer, and enough wariness to state that, while they still intended to use atmospheric traction and the broad gauge, they would adopt any gauge and means that would give them economy and high speed. And a new project, the Windsor, Staines, Brentford & London, to build a line to Knightsbridge, which proposed atmospheric traction for frequent trains, low costs, and freedom from noise and smoke, reserved the right to use locomotives, or a mixture of traction systems, as experience on other lines should suggest.

It all looked as strange to Brunel as it does to us : 'I returned only this afternoon and am endeavouring but very ineffectually as yet to comprehend the present extraordinary state of railway matters—when everybody around seems mad—stark staring wildly mad—the only course for a sane man is to get out of the way and keep quiet . . . I don't intend to go mad and I should soon at the rate others are going.'

In France, the end of 1844 had seen the adoption of Samuda's system on the last $5\frac{1}{2}$ miles of the Paris & St Germain railway, the section from Nanterre to the terrace of St Germain, with three stationary engines. Work went on here during 1845. In Belgium, late in the same year, A. Vifquain was seeking a concession for a 30 km line on Samuda's principle from Brussels to Louvain. Elsewhere abroad, perhaps Austria showed most interest in the new ideas. In 1844–45 a company to promote

Samuda's system on a Viennese suburban line was formed there, and Dr Karl Ritter von Ghega, the engineer for the Semmering route of the Southern Railway, then being considered, had it in mind for the steep northern ascent. In early 1845 the Austrians sent H. Schmidt, Inspector General of the Government Railways, to England to study it, then to return by way of France to see what was happening at St Germain. But political crises caused delays, and when the plans were taken up again, they were for a locomotive line. Vignoles had also recommended a double-track atmospheric line from Vienna to Schönbrunn, 7 miles long, with three engine-houses and gradients increasing to 1 in 30, to cope with up to 30,000 passengers in a four-hour period, during which both lines could be worked in the same direction. No action resulted.

In August the first trials were held on the Croydon line. Cubitt had done a creditable job to get the railway working in a year from the passing of the Act. After two months of learning to run trains in opposite directions on the same line by atmospheric power, and to co-ordinate his three stationary engines, problems that had not arisen at Dalkey, Cubitt was confident enough to lay on a run for shareholders on 20 October. But not until 19 January 1846 did he open to the public. By then the Croydon company had agreed to amalgamate with the London & Brighton, whose atmospheric enthusiasm was minimal, and who had, because of their links with the LSW, been hostile to the Direct London & Portsmouth. By then, also, there had been time for plenty of rumours of the operating difficulties that were being encountered, and of the lack of enthusiasm of the Croydon's prospective partners, to find their way into board-rooms and markets alike, though mostly too late to stop a small crop of bills for new atmospheric lines from being deposited.

The Direct London & Portsmouth spent the autumn negotiating an agreement with the Reading & Reigate Atmospheric Railway (which planned to build a line from Reading to Redhill), whereby the latter joined the DLP near Godalming, and the Portsmouth company would have running powers from Dorking to Reigate and over a proposed Guildford branch, so saving the DLP the cost of themselves building similar branches that Cubitt had earlier suggested. Wilkinson and de Castro then became directors of the Reading & Reigate. For the next session the nucleus of the London & Croydon's rejected bills of 1845 emerged again as a nominally independent company under W. A. Wilkinson's chairmanship, the Great Kent Atmospheric. Though an Act had been passed to extend the London & Brighton's Chichester branch to Portsmouth, the Direct London & Portsmouth again intended a bill, and were joined by the Edinburgh & Leith Atmospheric, the Dublin & Sandymount, the Windsor, Slough & Staines, and of course the South Devon's bills for branches to Torquay, Tavistock, and Exmouth.

If we were to put a date to the peak of excitement over the atmospheric system, it would be the autumn of 1845. After that the curve falls rapidly. To some extent the atmospheric had become identified in peoples' minds with the mania, and suffered correspondingly from the reaction. Again, there had seemed to be a touch of the miraculous about the new system. But this did not survive four months of testing on a line so near the centre of things as the London & Croydon. No longer did excited parties rush to Dalkey to be treated as distinguished guests, and have tests made for them upon the little Irish miracle. Instead, the testing went on under the eyes of the railway and general Press; things were seen to go wrong; stories from the staff began to circulate; and slowly people realised how young and untried the new principle still was, and how many practical problems still had to be solved. These things were enough to swing the national mood from extreme optimism to a pessimism and cynicism which well-disposed men and their journals found themselves inadequate to combat.

After the end of 1845 steam, for a moment threatened, returned triumphant; the atmospheric for a short time held its ground without making progress, then quickly fell.

CHAPTER FIVE

1846-1860

THE mania was over. The first half of 1846 was spent by shareholders in trying to get back the remnants of their deposits in companies that had failed to get their Acts, or had never tried, by Government in legislating to help them, and by ex-directors, promoters and solicitors in avoiding awkward questions from those inquiring where the money entrusted to them had gone.

And with the mania went belief in the future of the atmospheric system. It had been steadily evaporating during the Croydon's period of testing, and the first few weeks of public service after its shaky start on 19 January. Thenceforward there were to be no new proposals for atmospheric lines, a growing conviction that the Croydon and South Devon were doomed, a diminution of interest and of serious comment in the railway press, continuing denigration by Herapath, and a kind of exasperation with Cubitt and Brunel for persisting so long in what were clearly to be failures. The bills before Parliament in 1846 were the result of the enthusiasm of 1845. The failure of all but one of them was much more the result than the cause of this change of opinion, which we can date to the last two months of the mania year and the first three of the next. In this the spies played a part.

George Hudson was a determined opponent of atmospheric railways, while Robert Stephenson and Joseph Locke knew that they would be called upon to give evidence against them in the 1846 session. Between them they employed three gentlemen, Messrs Robertson, Winter, and Wright, to travel on and watch the London & Croydon, and to collect damaging data. John Winter, for instance, for five weeks from 2 February travelled on 24 trains a day on the Croydon, noting train weights, delays of any kind, and whether any trains were locomotive-hauled. He also recorded the staff employed and their wages, and found out the coal consumption and the price paid. His findings were passed round engineering circles and to editors, and caused clearly intended confusion. For instance, in May 1847 the editor of *The Builder* referred to 'the extraordinary discrepancies and deviations in statement and counterstatement, respecting the progress of the atmospheric system, which have hitherto perplexed the impartial chronicler of events'. They were also produced to Parliamentary committees such as that on the Exeter, Topsham & Exmouth atmospheric branch of the South Devon, which was also considering the competing Exeter & Exmouth for which Locke was engineer. Winter's figures were correct enough, but they needed much more commentary than they received, and therefore disproportionately damaged the atmospheric case, though on this occasion Locke was forced to admit that he himself had never inspected the Croydon line, but had only seen it from the carriage window of a Brighton train.

Let us now look at the pending bills. The one that succeeded was the Direct London & Portsmouth. This was to run from the end of the Croydon's Epsom extension to Dorking, Godalming and then roughly along the present Portsmouth line. At the year's beginning the company had rejected overtures from the London & South Western for an accommodation, made after an LSW meeting at which it had been said : 'It is well known now that the atmospheric system was a failure, owing to the cost of working it . . . the cost of getting up the steam power to work a hundred tons was so great that no line upon this principle could ever pay more than $2\frac{1}{2}$ or 3 per cent', and went ahead against a rival project, the Guildford, Chichester & Portsmouth, supported by the Brighton and LSW companies.

In April, however, the Brighton was faced with a new situation as a result of its proposed amalgamation with the London & Croydon, backing the Direct London & Portsmouth. Talks began, and in May the Brighton abandoned their support for the Guildford, Chichester & Portsmouth, which failed to get its Act, and agreed that should the DLP's bill pass, two-thirds of the capital would be subscribed by the Brighton and Croydon companies, and one-third by the DLP shareholders taking London & Brighton stock. The DLP would thus become a wholly-owned subsidiary of what was soon to be the London, Brighton & South Coast Railway. It was also agreed that, if required, the London & Brighton would use their influence with the Brighton & Chichester for a single atmospheric line for the DLP alongside their tracks between Havant and Portsmouth.

The Direct London & Portsmouth's Act passed, just in time for the last meeting of the independent London & Croydon company, which had done so much to promote it. Agreement with the Brighton & Chichester and the London & Brighton on the Havant–Portsmouth line followed, and Joseph Cubitt was instructed to start setting out. But financial pressure was now showing itself, to reinforce the Brighton's lack of enthusiasm for things atmospheric. In July Ricardo resigned from the DLP's board; in September land was bought; in October the LSW agreed to participate with the LBSC in the DLP. In December de Castro also resigned, a sign that atmospheric traction had finally been dropped. In 1847 a bill to amalgamate the DLP with the LBSC was lost, and thereafter the company fell dormant, the LBSC and the LSW having agreed to pool their receipts from London–Portsmouth traffic by their own roundabout routes. Its last meeting was held on 25 May 1855, still presided over by W. A. Wilkinson, a shadowy reminder of earlier times. By then an Act of 1853 had authorised a new direct line from Godalming to Havant. It was opened in 1859.

There had been an early proposal for an atmospheric line from Dorking to Reigate, which had been dropped by mid–1845. The more ambitious Reading and Reigate Atmospheric then appeared with a capital of £800,000 to build a line from the Great Western at Reading to the LSW at Farnborough, and then to Dorking, Reigate, and Redhill on the London & Brighton and the South Eastern. In February 1846 they amalgamated with the non-atmospheric Reading, Guildford & Reigate, negotiated running powers over 5 miles of the DLP's line between Dorking and Gomshall, and dropped atmospheric traction. The combined company, which had agreed to lease itself to the SER on completion, was incorporated in July 1846, built its line by October 1849, and was taken over by the South Eastern in 1852.

The Great Kent Atmospheric, also with W. A. Wilkinson as chairman, had been formed in the autumn of 1845 to take over the London & Croydon's Kent interests, and, with a capital of £2½ million to promote 130 miles of atmospheric line from the London & Croydon to Maidstone, Canterbury, and Dover, and to Gravesend with branches to Tonbridge, Ashford, Faversham, Deal, Sandwich, and Rochester. By January 1846 they had succeeded in raising £107,000 in deposits on 43,040 shares out of the 92,000 allotted, but £182,000 was needed if they were to go forward with a bill; so they tried to get the rest from the London & Croydon and the London & Brighton. Cubitt was set to examine their estimates, and advised the London & Croydon that the GKA would not be safe to go to Parliament without greatly increasing them. If, as he considered, that railway's committee reduced its ideas to a line to Maidstone and Tonbridge, or at most Ashford, they would not need help.

The terms proposed by the L & C and L & B were therefore discouraging, and so the GKA agreed with the North Kent Railway, also seeking a bill, that the former should only apply for a Maidstone and Tonbridge line, relinquished the rest of their proposals to the North Kent. Should the latter get an Act, certain payments were to be made to the GKA. In fact, both bills went down before the South Eastern's mid-Kent line. The Great Kent then gave up, arranging to hand their plans to the London, Brighton & South Coast in exchange for the repayment by that company of £2 each to GKA shareholders out of the 50s they had deposited, in spite of the fact that more than the 10s promised as an expense limit had in fact been spent.

The idea that became the Windsor, Slough & Staines was launched in 1844 as the Windsor Junction, with Thomas Page

WINDSOR, SLOUGH, AND STAINES
ATMOSPHERIC RAILWAY.

CAPITAL, £150,000,

IN 7,500 SHARES, OF £20 EACH.—DEPOSIT, £2 2s. PER SHARE.

Provisionally Registered pursuant to 7 and 8 Vic., c. 110.

Provisional Committee.

JOHN RAMSBOTTOM, Esq., M.P. *for Windsor.*

RALPH NEVILLE, Esq., M.P. *for Windsor.*

JAMES THOMAS BEDBOROUGH, Esq., *Upton Park, near Windsor.*

JEREMIAH PILCHER, Esq., *Russell-square, late Sheriff of London, Director of the Paris and Strasbourg Railway.*

LEWIS POCOCK, Esq., *Montague-street, Russell-square, Director of the Reading and Reigate Railway, and the Argus Life Assurance Company.*

JOHN EDWARDS LANGTON, Esq., *Maidenhead.*

FREDERICK FOWLER, Esq., *Windsor.*

JOSEPH CARRINGTON RIDGWAY, Esq., *Roehampton Lodge, Surrey, one of the Provisional Committee of the Exeter, Dorchester, and Weymouth Junction Coast Railway.*

JOHN FOWLER, Esq., *Southleys House, Datchet.*

SIR RAYMOND JARVIS, *Fair Oak Park, Winchester.*

VALENTINE KNIGHT, Esq., 3, *Cornwall Terrace, Regent's Park.*

WILLIAM VERNON STEPHENS, Esq., *Birkins Manor House, Horton.*

WILLIAM BERRIDGE, Esq., *Windsor.*

JOHN BRADLEY SHUTTLEWORTH, Esq., 33, *Eastcheap, London.*

CALEB NORRIS, Esq., *Lancaster-place, London, one of the Provisional Committee of the Exeter, Dorchester, and Weymouth Junction Coast Railway.*

RICHARD IBOTSON, Esq., *Poyle Mills, near Horton.*

ALFRED FOWLER, Esq., *Datchet, Bucks.*

ROBERT OWEN ALAND, Esq., *Greek-street, Soho.*

SAMUEL DAVIS, Esq., *Brunswick Terrace, Windsor.*

MR. JOHN ROBERTS, *Windsor.*

MR. WILLIAM HENRY BURGE, *Windsor.*

MR. WILLIAM WEAVER BERRIDGE, *Windsor.*

MR. JOHN CLODE, Jun., *Windsor.*

WITH POWER TO ADD TO THEIR NUMBER.

Engineer.
CHARLES VIGNOLES, ESQ,, F.R.A.S. M.R,I.A.

Solicitors.
MESSRS. DARVILL & GEARY, WINDSOR.

Bankers.
MESSRS. WILLIAMS, DEACON, & Co., LONDON. | MESSRS. NEVILE REID & Co., WINDSOR.

Secretary, pro tem.
MR. HENRY COOK, WINDSOR.

PROSPECTUS.

This Railway is intended to remedy the great inconvenience and delay at present existing in the communication between the towns of Windsor and Eton, and the Great Western Railway, and also to obtain the advantages proposed by the Staines and Richmond Lines of Railway to a London Terminus at Hungerford Bridge, with such other facilities as may be opened up by any of the proposed Lines proceeding from the West-end of London towards Windsor.

An atmospheric railway prospectus

a, the cam ; *b b*, the breaks ; *c c*, levers by which the locking of the other wheels is effected.

IX. *(above) The cam brake used on the Croydon piston carriages; (below) a contemporary sketch of the crossings installed by Cubitt at Forest Hill station to move not only points, but sections of rail out of the piston's way; the lever required six men to move it*

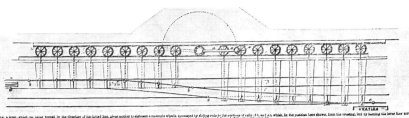

a w, a lever, which, on being turned in the direction of the dotted line, gives motion to eighteen concentric wheels, connected by sliding rods to the portions of rails ; *b b*, and *c c*, which, in the position here shown, form the crossing, but by turning the lever they are brought to the position indicated by dotted lines ; *d*, the end of the atmospheric tube.

MR. WILLIAM CUBITT'S APPARATUS FOR AN ATMOSPHERIC CROSSING.

x. *A telegraph operator on the Croydon line. The telegraph connected
the engine-houses at Forest Hill, Norwood and Croydon*

as engineer, to build a railway from Windsor to Slough or Lang-
ley and Datchet to join the Great Western and projected Richmond lines. A private station was to be provided for the royal
family, and atmospheric traction was proposed because of its
cleanliness, using a single engine-house of pleasing character at
the half-way point. An application was made to the Commissioners of Woods and Forests. They, however, would give no
opinion until a bill had been lodged, and by mid-1845 the
scheme had been overtaken by others. One was the Windsor,
Staines, Brentford & London, with George Rennie as engineer,
promoted in mid-1845, but which went no further. Another was
the Windsor, Slough & Staines, with Charles Vignoles as
engineer and a capital of £150,000, to build from Windsor
bridge one atmospheric line to the Great Western at Slough, and
another via Datchet to Staines on the London & South Western.
An 18 in tube was to be used, with three engine-houses, two with
a total of 130 hp, and one of 150 hp. Thirty trains a day were
envisaged between Windsor and Slough, twenty to and from
Staines. Vignoles' diary records that on 21 November 1845 he
'attended the meeting at Windsor on the Windsor Atmospheric
Railway. Arranging the proper models and drawings for the in-
spection of Her Majesty.'

A bill for this was introduced in 1846, but went down before
the combined onslaught of the Great Western, the Woods and
Forests, and the Provost and Fellows of Eton College, Dr
Hawtrey telling the Lords committee that the line would prove
an obstacle to the strict discipline of his school. The rejected company at first proposed to accept a Great Western offer to share
in a branch from Slough to Windsor, but then changed their
minds and amalgamated with the Staines & Richmond to form
the Windsor, Staines & South Western (Richmond to Windsor).
This was incorporated in 1847, not as an atmospheric line, and
reached Datchet in 1848. It was allowed into Windsor in December 1849.

In Scotland, the Edinburgh, Leith & Granton Railway had
in August 1842 opened $1\frac{1}{4}$ miles of line from the chain pier at

F

Leith to the bottom of Scotland Street, Edinburgh. A year later passenger traffic had much increased, and extensions were in hand from Scotland Street through a tunnel to join the Edinburgh & Glasgow and North British lines at Princes Street, and also from the existing line to Leith docks and Granton pier.

Construction was going on when in October 1845 there were two schemes for an atmospheric line between Edinburgh and Leith. One, the Edinburgh & Leith Atmospheric, engineered by John Miller, proposed to build a line wholly under cover, with five stopping places in Edinburgh—Princes Street, St Andrew Street, York Place, Leith Terrace and Catherine Street. Then the line 'will proceed by Leith Walk . . . and at the foot . . . will branch off to the Upper Drawbridge, to the Lower Draw-bridge, and also to the Wharf at the Old-Ferry-Boat Stairs, with intermediate stations at the Exchange Buildings, and other points that may be found necessary'. The main line was $1\frac{7}{8}$ miles long with a maximum gradient of 1 in 40; the branches added 5 furlongs more. Operation was to be upwards by atmospheric power, downwards by gravity, though possible locomotive work-ing was provided for. Therefore the line, though double track, would have only one tube, with the engine-house at the summit. They had the support of some Edinburgh & Glasgow Railway directors, and later announced an alliance with the North British Railway 'for the use of their Terminus, and access to their Rails, at the North Bridge, Edinburgh, and for the use of their pro-posed Depot, and access to their Rails at Leith', as well as for interchange of goods traffic. North British support to their bill was also promised, which, they warned, was likely to be opposed by the Edinburgh, Leith & Granton company.

The other, the Edinburgh & Leith Atmospheric Direct, which claimed to have been the first in the field, had a capital of £200,000. Its engineer, George Gunn, proposed to link the towns by a direct line $1\frac{7}{8}$ miles long, most of it in tunnel, from Leith Quay to West Register Street, Edinburgh, with a $\frac{1}{4}$ mile branch to the North British Railway at Princes Street, the steepest gradient being 1 in 29. Preference in allotment of shares was promised to shareholders of the North British and Caledonian Railways. This line also proposed to use atmospheric traction upwards and gravity downwards, though later they protected themselves by saying that 'the Company do not thereby preclude themselves from employing the ordinary locomotive principle, should that be considered more expedient'. The Direct withdrew after a promise from the rival company to pay them £1,000 towards their expenses if an Act were obtained, and the Atmospheric went ahead. A deputation of directors went to London, travelled on the Croydon, and were encouraged that a 5 minute service might be run, though Samuda in evidence on the bill proposed one of 10 minutes. Land for termini was bought, but the Edinburgh, Leith & Granton's branch to Leith had opened in May 1846, and the Atmospheric's bill was lost after about £11,000 had been spent out of the £20,000 received in deposits on their capital of £200,000. In the end shareholders got back 32s out of each 40s.

The Dublin & Sandymount had been promoted at the end of 1845 by a group of prominent Dublin people, to build a single 2 mile long commuter and excursion line, much of it on arches, from Great Brunswick Street not far from the Dublin & Kingstown's station to Sandymount by the sea. It was estimated to yield 17 per cent on a cost of some £80,000, and 6,000 shares were allotted, though the autumn panic meant that deposits were paid only on 3,200. Thinking they had received informal assurances of Dublin & Kingstown neutrality, they went ahead to register their company. After they had done so, Sir John Macneill was appointed engineer, and recommended a locomotive railway. This, then, was the project that went to Parliament, though the word 'Atmospheric' was still in the company's title. Then appeared a parliamentary notice for the Dublin & Kingstown to build a branch from the canal docks at Dublin to Sandymount, that company explaining when questioned that they had not formally known of the atmospheric project. The Dublin & Sandymount went on with their bill, however, got it through the Lords, then lost it in the Commons committee mainly to Dublin & Kingstown opposition. Though a meeting in May 1846 decided to try again, nothing more was done.

Of the other bills, the South Devon succeeded with its atmospheric branch to Torquay (Torre), but not with that for the $7\frac{1}{2}$ mile line across the Exe at Countess Wear and on to Topsham and Exmouth, in spite of Brunel and Samuda's explanations that atmospheric trains could be worked over the proposed drawbridge over the Exe, or with that to Tavistock which had been stood over from the year before. Finally, the Cornwall got its Act, but there were few who seriously expected it to use the atmospheric.

In January M. Hallette, who in 1845 had sent an agent to England to push his system, began to build an experimental atmospheric line, 400 ft long with a 5 in tube, in the grounds of the 'Rosemary Branch' at Peckham, along which a carriage carrying four people would be propelled at 10 to 12 mph. This was opened in May and ran three days a week for four hours a day, free tickets being obtainable from the office of Hallette's Atmospheric Railway & Canal Propulsion Company at Winchester House, Old Broad Street. A fourth day was added for a time.

Hallette, France's biggest steam-engine maker, had become interested in atmospheric traction, worked out an alternative type of longitudinal valve to lessen leakage and enable stationary engines to be put as far as $5\frac{1}{4}$ miles apart, and laid down an experimental 300 ft of track at his Arras works. The trials were satisfactory, and he patented his valve. Instead of hinged leather, he used two hollow rubber pipes inflated with compressed air at 5 psi and covered with cotton and leather. These lay over the slot in the tube, and pressed so hard against each other that, except when opened by the piston, leakage was much reduced.

Cubitt went over to France and saw the experiments at Arras. He told the Select Committee that the test length worked well, and he could detect no leakage, but that in his view Hallette's valve would be better applied to raising minerals out of deep mines, with Clegg and Samuda's used for railways. He added, however, that it seemed a pity that Samuda was trying to sell his system in France, as tests of both would be useful. When it became clear that Clegg and Samuda's valve was seriously affected by the weather, Hallette's was offered as an alternative.

In January also, R. Addams was lecturing on atmospheric railways to the Birmingham Philosophical Institution, a public meeting in Portsmouth denied that the delay in completing the Croydon & Epsom line and the difficulties on the Croydon had destroyed the confidence of the Portsmouth people in atmospheric traction, and Parsey advertised his Compressed Air Engine Company, to build locomotives costing about half as much as steam ones, and which did not need atmospheric tubes. The curious could see a working model.

In the same month the *Pictorial Times* carried a small news item which foreshadowed, if contemporaries had realised it, the eventual traction solution for commuter traffic: 'Experiments of a highly satisfactory character are being made with regard to the application of electro-magnetism to railway propulsion. The great difficulty to be surmounted is the weight and size of the galvanic batteries requisite for sufficient energy. To obviate this difficulty it has been proposed to have stationary batteries at regulated distances, and to make the rails themselves the conducting lines of the batteries.' Some contemporaries did. The far-sighted George Gill, jnr, writing in the *Western Times* on 17 September 1847, said: 'The locomotive engine is in itself so perfect, that we must go into the next century ere we find anything to surpass it, and then perchance magnetic attraction, with a succession of changing poles, will be the power.'

In February Samuda agreed with the LBSC to work the Croydon line on contract, and was accused by Herapath of having taken it on to keep the Croydon open long enough to get the South Devon's public service going, so that he could draw the patent payment. This is a good example of Herapath's worst side, for only £250 a mile, or £3,750, was payable, and for such a sum it was certainly not worth while Samuda risking real trouble on the Croydon. A fortnight later we get a glimpse of the other side of Herapath's character. For years he had attacked, poked fun at, vilified W. A. Wilkinson. Yet 'Mr W. A. Wilkinson, a correspondent informs us, intends to go into the House for Canterbury . . . there is, and will be, many men in the House of much less ability, of much less private worth, and, we believe, of much less public honesty. We, therefore, hesitate not to wish him success; but mind, we don't a bit the more agree with him about the atmospheric nonsense'.

In February also the Royal Institute of British Architects told their hopeful but perhaps bemused members that plans had been deposited and standing orders had been complied with for 21 schemes for railway termini in the City, and the Report of the Railway Gauge Commissioners appeared. It was adverse to the broad gauge, and with its publication there broke out a brisk battle of letters and pamphlets in which the broad-gauge supporters found themselves outnumbered, out-argued and on the defensive. This in turn encouraged attacks on the Brunellites. Thus, for instance, the *Railway Times*: 'the western sect, which flings its dividends and its fares beneath the gigantic wheels of the railway idol . . . if we were about to construct a railway regardless of expense, for the express use of kings and conquerors, and their attendant armies, we would certainly adopt the broad gauge . . . we prefer convenience and economy to high charges and overpowering size'. And on Brunel: 'we do not take him for either a rogue or a fool, but an enthusiast, blinded by the light of his own genius —an engineering knight-errant, always on the look-out for magic caves to be penetrated and enchanted rivers to be crossed—never so happy as when "engaged regardless of cost" in conquering some, to ordinary mortals, impossibility; always intent rather on the applause of posterity than on the half-yearly dividends of his shareholders—fitter minister of an imperial despot than the adviser of a commercial company'.

One effect of the broad-gauge controversy was to undermine confidence in the atmospheric system in the south-west even before it was tried, because it was Brunel's and because he was associated with the broad-gauge. The atmospheric Exeter, Topsham & Exmouth had failed. In May, at a meeting of the Cornwall Railway, which had not yet formally decided not to use atmospheric traction should it prove successful on the South Devon, Mr Woollcombe said that Brunel had written that 'he entertained the same opinion he before held as to the applicability of the atmospheric system; and after having attentively followed the proceedings on the Croydon line, he considered the results quite confirmatory of that opinion. The experiment on the Croydon line had fully succeeded, although the circumstances of the line of railway being incomplete, rendered the working comparatively inconvenient.' *Besley's Devonshire Chronicle* chimed in that 'the South Devon may look forward with confidence to a complete and lasting triumph over those who have sneered at, and wish to cry down the line and the principle together'. But who was now giving Brunel's words the weight they would have carried in 1844?

When the South Devon opened to Teignmouth on 30 May, with seven trains to and from Exeter timed to do the journey in 45 minutes, and three on Sundays, it was with locomotives. The *Railway Times*, with Brunellism in mind, commented: 'When the atmospheric portion of the line will be ready for operation is quite a matter of uncertainty. Anyone who takes the trouble to glance at the immense engine-houses, and the massive machinery which is required, will see that a very long time must elapse before the actual day for bringing this apparatus into operation can be decided on.'

In May Charles Collins of London and Kidderminster went bankrupt with a choice collection of worthless railway shares, one of many victims of the mania: 'having unfortunately given up business as a merchant, which I conducted successfully for twenty years, to embark in these visions of riches, I have lost my all, and have now to commence the work again'. He had been the secretary of Pilbrow's company in 1845, as well as the inventor of a variant of Pilbrow's system, and among his assets were a quarter interest of the balance of £14,000 due to Pilbrow for his English patent rights from Pilbrow's Railway & Canal Propulsion Company, and a quarter interest in Pilbrow's Foreign Patent Railway & Canal Company, which had agreed to buy these Pilbrow rights for £90,000, to be paid when 50 miles of line on his principle had been laid down. The Pilbrow companies do not seem to have been run with much financial exactitude, and critically hopeful gatherings of the shareholders took place on 11 and 17 August. The English company had had a difference of opinion with the inventor upon the price they had to pay for his English patent: he had received £45,000 in shares and £1,000 in cash, but claimed £14,000 more—presumably Collins had lent him some ready money against a quarter share of this claim. It was intended to issue 60,000 £10 shares, but as only £4,570 had been received in deposits, the future did not look promising. It was probably another Mr Collins who toured the country demonstrating the electric telegraph, a model atmospheric railway, and other scientific novelties. His model, with a 1½ in tube and a hand-pump, could move a carriage carrying 'the heaviest person who cares to take a seat in it'. It seems to have been a great success at the Mechanics Hall at Chesterfield.

The English patent rights in Hallette's valve had been sold to a much more respectable London company for £6,500 cash and £3,000 in shares. Mr J. Brightman in the chair said, however, that a line upon which to try the invention had not yet been found. He referred more hopefully to other uses for it, to the vast superiority it possessed over existing methods for traction in mines, and also as a means of ventilation. Other inventors were also busy, as he who proposed discontinuous impulses, 'working by short close tubes of enlarged calibre, placed at intervals along the line, by which the train is propelled from station to station . . . a mile or so of tube will work 100 miles of rail'. A diagram of the pipework to connect the tubes to the engines, and an explanation of what happened if the train stopped between tubes, seem alike required.

In May Samuda put an advertisement in letter form into *The*

Times to contradict a statement of Herapath's about working costs on the Dalkey: 'I have always treated with contempt the repeated and unscrupulous assertions put forward by the journalist referred to . . . for the purpose of injuring the system in public estimation'; in May also the Croydon had felt confident enough to expand the service on its atmospheric line to 19 down and 20 up trains each weekday, mostly all stations, but with 3 down and 4 up trains stopping at Forest Hill only, and one each way at Forest Hill and Sydenham. All trains carried first, second, and third class passengers. But at the end of the month the service had to be shut down for six weeks. The thin steel plates covering the leather of the valve, which Samuda had considered such an improvement, tended to snap off; the sharp broken edges then cut into the valve leather beneath, causing leakages and breakdowns. So the whole valve had to be removed, and double leathers on the Dalkey plan substituted. At the same time the composition previously used had not stood up to the very hot summer weather, and a new one was introduced. The shut-down demonstrated how much still had to be learned by experience: passengers were annoyed, and the London & Croydon's shareholders saw their costs mounting.

Once more the invention suffered a personal loss it could ill afford. Jacob Samuda had gone, and now Hallette, on his way back to France from negotiating the English sale of his patent, was taken ill at Boulogne and died a few days later. Soon his engine works would be up for sale.

August brought the LBSC in place of the old Croydon and Brighton companies, and a board no longer enthusiastic for atmospheric working. By the late autumn it was known that the real trouble on the Croydon, underlying valve and composition difficulties, was a tube too small in diameter and engines too low in power, and that the Epsom extension would be locomotive worked. This, and the final failure of the Great Kent Atmospheric to get an Act, put William Wilkinson's stock low. The *Railway Times*, who had never liked him, said: 'Through such straits and enormities has he gone with respect to this Kent affair, and so strenuously has he blown the Kent atmospheric trumpet, that throughout the country he has acquired the very expressive appellation of Windy Wilkinson.'

Henceforward the story is that of the four railways. In February 1847 the London & Croydon's atmospheric line was extended for nearly three miles to New Cross, though everyone knew that its power was inadequate for working heavy suburban trains up the long incline to Forest Hill. On 24 April the French line started atmospheric traction over the three kilometres between Bois de Vésinet and Saint Germain. Ten days later the Croydon went over to steam. In September the South Devon began to run atmospheric trains between Exeter and Teignmouth, extending these to Newton in January 1848 partially, and in February as a complete service. This Exeter to Newton run was twenty miles, the greatest length of line ever worked atmospherically.

On Wednesday 6 September 1848 Samuda's hopes fell in ruins, when the South Devon went over to locomotives. Yet, in Ireland, the Dalkey kept on running year after year, except for a two months gap when the air-pump fractured, till it closed on Wednesday 12 April 1854 for no failure of the system, but for gauge conversion and rebuilding before integration in a wider railway system. Last of all, in France the Saint Germain line, having survived until 1860, went over to steam on 3 July because increasing traffic meant that it could be better worked with locomotives. So Clegg and Samuda's system ended, though with T. W. Rammell the atmospheric was for a time revived in the earlier forms of Vallance and Medhurst.

Clegg hardly appears throughout the whole atmospheric controversy. Yet he felt its failure deeply, so much so that he was afterwards hardly heard of until his death on 8 January 1861, aged 79. Joseph Samuda developed the firm of Samuda Bros. as large iron shipbuilders, constructing ironclad warships for the British and foreign navies, and also such craft as Channel steamers. In the sixties he became a member of the Metropolitan Board of Works, the predecessor of the London County Council, and between 1865 and 1880 Liberal member for

Parliament first for Tavistock and later for Tower Hamlets. He died in London in April 1885.

Beside the short chronicle of dates we have nothing to set of modern, and little of contemporary, interest. Inventors of new types of valve lived, experimented, and were ignored, for who wanted to burn their fingers again? There were Clarke and Varley, who in the spring of 1847 laid down 250 yd of 15 in tube beside the London & Blackwall at Poplar to experiment with their valve. William Turnbull liked it. He was the author of a thoughtful little book published in 1847, *An Essay on the Air-Pump and Atmospheric Railway*, which, taking Robert Stephenson's report as a starting point, set out to give engineering students the technical background of atmospheric practice.

Turnbull considered that no scheme for improving the valve would eliminate leaks, and that the problem must be solved in some such way as Clarke and Varley's. A sheet-iron tube, planed at the edges and chamfered to an angle, was bent into cylindrical shape, 'a form which induces a tendency to close, in consequence of the elasticity of the material, assisted by the external pressure of the atmosphere, so that the edges of the plate are brought together with a slight force, and form a perfectly air-tight cylindrical tube'. Along the outside of the tube on each side ran continuous wrought-iron bars connected to it, supported on brackets, and strong enough to resist the elasticity of the tube. A 'traveller' on the piston carriage would have four rollers a little wider than the bars, operating in pairs. These would force the bars about $\frac{3}{4}$ in apart and so open the tube, which would close after each train by its own elasticity. W. B. Hays, engineer to the patentees, tried to sell this system to the South Devon in February 1848, but was refused an interview or a trial.

There were many others: from Cunningham and Carter's sets of trackside wheels powered by an underground tube and actuated by an approaching train, a $7\frac{1}{4}$ in gauge scale-model of which was working at the Waterworks, Peak Hill, Sydenham, in September 1847, to Weston's Novamotive Railway, patented in 1848 by a mechanic after he and twenty working-class friends had spent £1,000, and publicised by the *Christian Socialist* to raise enough money to show it at the Great Exhibition. But they do not matter.

Today, over the ground where once ran fast, frequent Croydon commuter trains driven from lineside engine-houses through a piston running in a tube between the rails, run fast, frequent commuter trains, driven from stationary power-stations through a shoe picking up current from a third rail. Would Robert Stephenson have called the method a rope of electricity, as he called the atmospheric a rope of air, and would he now have been a diesel man, as Samuda would undoubtedly have been an electricity man? And who would have been right? Mobile power or stationary power? The debate continues into our own future.

CHAPTER SIX

LATIMER CLARK AND RAMMELL

ONE story had ended, but two new ones were beginning : the use of atmospheric pressure, with or without that of compressed air also, on the one hand for postal and telegraph tubes, on the other for underground railways.

In 1853 J. Latimer Clark laid down an atmospherically-operated tube 675 ft long and of 1½ in diameter, worked by a 6 hp engine, to carry felt bags containing bundles of urgent messages between the Electrical & International Telegraph Company's station in Telegraph Street, London, and their branch at the Stock Exchange. The first little tube gave the Post Office an idea, and in 1855 they commissioned two engineers to report whether it was practicable to convey mails by atmospheric pressure in a tube between the General Post Office and a point near the corner of Little Queen Street and Holborn, which was to be the site of the West Central district office. One was a man of some atmospheric experience, our old friend Charles H. Gregory, formerly of the London & Croydon; the other, Edward A. Cowper. They reported in 1855 and 1856 that such a tube would be practicable, especially if it were of 15 in diameter, but would be expensive. The cost seemed too high to the Post Office, who then dropped the idea.

In 1858 the Telegraph Company built another small tube, 3,120 ft long and 2¼ in diameter. About 1865 Latimer Clark engineered, and Siemens constructed, two tubes each 2,835 ft long and 3½ in diameter between the Exchange and Central Telegraph stations in Berlin, atmospheric pressure being used to send messages in one, and compressed air those travelling the opposite way in the other. About that time, however, probably as a result of Latimer Clark's co-operation with T. W. Rammell on tube railways, it had become possible to use both atmospheric and positive pressure for travel in opposite directions in one tube, though this meant pumping out the tube each time a carrier with its message had been dispatched. This difficulty was overcome in 1870 by J. W. Willmott with his double sluice valve. Carriers could now be dispatched continuously, and postal and telegraph tubes quickly developed.

By 1874 our own Post Office had put in an extensive system to carry telegrams between the central telegraph office at St Martin's le Grand and London district post offices. Many miles of lead tubes encased in iron pipes were laid in pairs under the streets to take carriers 8 in long by $1\frac{1}{2}$ in diameter travelling at 20 mph, propelled either by compressed air at up to 12 psi or atmospheric pressure of $6\frac{1}{2}$ psi, according to the direction of travel, and powered by three 50 hp compound beam engines at St Martin's. By 1886 London had 94 tubes totalling $34\frac{1}{2}$ miles, powered by four 50 hp engines. There were other installations at Liverpool, Manchester, Birmingham, Glasgow, Newcastle upon Tyne, and Dublin, the whole British system having 129 tubes, $45\frac{1}{2}$ miles long, powered by 14 engines, and sending 51,478 messages a day through tubes $1\frac{1}{2}$ to 3 in diameter. These street tubes were supplemented at large telegraph offices by house tubes to pass telegraph forms from one part of the building to another.

In Europe similar systems for telegrams, or on a rather larger scale for postcards and small letters paying a special fee, were built in Paris (including a tube thence to Versailles), Berlin, Vienna, and in Italy. In the United States the first mail tube, half a mile long and 6 in diameter, was opened at Philadelphia in 1893. By 1897 there were 8 miles of 8 in tubes in New York, Brooklyn, Boston, and Philadelphia, and by 1908 these and other cities had $42\frac{1}{2}$ miles, with 22 miles more under contract.

These developments in turn led to others, for instance, to pneumatic methods of carrying the stiff tickets used in trunk telephone exchanges between the operators and the filing positions, or of establishing central cash control in shops by means of the familiar tubes and containers carrying money between counters and cashier. Today, these systems are still in use in the telegraph and telephone services and, indeed, pneumatic tube communication is being installed as I write at the Savings Certificates Division of the Post Office Savings Bank's new premises at Durham.

George Medhurst would have been most gratified.

T. W. Rammell was an engineer who sought a modern answer to problems of urban transport which in his time, as in ours, were becoming increasingly urgent. In a pamphlet of 1857, *A New Plan for Street Railways*, he first suggested atmospherically-propelled overhead railways running on a circular track. A line of single iron columns was to carry the 3 ft 9 in gauge line and its long, low, eight-wheeled bogie coaches served by platforms accessible from the street by staircases.

Traction was by a development of Samuda's system. An underground ring tube connected at intervals to reserve chambers would be kept continuously exhausted by the stationary engines. A vacuum would therefore always be available to the traction tube between the rails, to which it would be connected at intervals. The power provided would be ample to work frequent lightweight 10–20 ton trains at up to 20 mph. The valve would not be closed by a composition, but 'rather by the compression of an elastic substance of which the edge of the valve will be formed against a smooth metal surface, placed in a nearly vertical position, the requisite pressure being given by a wheel running over the valve immediately behind the piston'.

Rammell must then have met Latimer Clark, heard of the investigation Gregory and Cowper had made for the Post Office, and realised that message tubes could be developed into tube railways to carry mails and also passengers. He and Clark now took Medhurst's idea of using compressed air in one direction and atmospheric pressure in the other, with the train itself as a piston, and adapted it to work with a stationary steam engine, a large reversible fan, and very low air pressure or vacuum. Going one way, the train would be pushed by air driven by the

fan into the tube; going the other, by atmospheric pressure because the fan, running in reverse, was now exhausting the air in
front of it.

A plan was developed and published to build a network of
underground mail and parcel-carrying railways stretching from
Shoreditch to Paddington and Waterloo to Euston, linking ten
district post offices with the General Post Office, and railway
stations to carriers' depots and markets, at a cost estimated at
£30,000 to £35,000 a mile. On 13 August 1859 the Pneumatic
Despatch Company, which had been formed with a board that
included Mark Huish, Thomas Brassey, and W. H. Smith, and had
the Duke of Buckingham and Chandos as chairman, obtained an
Act enabling it to lay tubes within the Metropolitan Board of
Works area.

Experiments were now made with Rammell's system, first at
the Soho works in Birmingham, and then in the summer of 1861
on a larger scale in Battersea Fields: 'on the river margin adjoin-
ing the Battersea station of the Brighton Railway . . . may now
be observed a black, sinuous object, more like a ribbed worm
than anything else, sometimes completely buried, then rising a
few feet, and again curving out of sight', a tube 30 in wide by
33 in high, and 452 yd long, provided with curves up to 300
ft radius, gradients up to 1 in 22, and terminal equipment.
Track of 24 in gauge was cast inside it, on which ran close-
fitting cars with hoods at one end fitted with vulcanised rubber
flaps to make an air seal. Power came from a 30 hp engine and a
21 ft diameter fan. Single cars and trains carrying weights up
to three tons, and even some intrepid passengers, were passed
through the tube at speeds up to 40 mph, using pressures of 1
to 6 oz/sq in.

The experiments were considered successful, and negotiations
began with the Post Office and railway companies for the building of a working line. The company naturally wished 'to obtain
a guarantee, or such arrangements for traffic, as will secure even
this first section being remunerative', but the Post Office would
not go further than to say that if a short tube was built for

River Exe   Haccombe   Railway Bridge   Engine House   Exeter Railway Station

xi. *The South Devon Railway in 1848: (above) Exeter St Davids, Bristol & Exeter station on the extreme right, South Devon station and engine-house in the centre, and Exe bridge to the left; (below) the engine-house at Countess Wear*

Countess Wear Viaduct   Engine House   Countess Wear Bridge   Lime Kilns

Turf House and entrance to the Exeter Canal   Woodbury Hill   Tank and Engine House

XII. *The South Devon Railway in 1848: (above) Turf engine-house and the entrance lock and basin of the Exeter Canal; (below) Dawlish, with the engine-house to the right*

Eastern face of the Kennaway Tunnel   Houses on the Teignmouth Road   Dawlish Beach   Engine House and Station   M. Powell's Villa   Langstone

about one-third of a mile from the arrival platform at Euston station to the North Western district post office in Eversholt Street, they would use it regularly so long as either side could end the arrangement at short notice. This was then constructed as a 30 in wide tube, as at Battersea, with a stationary engine at Euston.

The first tests were made on 15 January 1863, and on 20 February it was officially inaugurated, when Post Office officials watched 35 mailbags which had arrived at Euston on the 9.45 a.m. mail-train put on cars at 9.47 and reach Eversholt Street one minute later. Thereafter about 13 trains a day were reliably operated in either direction, carrying one to thirty mailbags each. The company seems to have made only a nominal charge for working the line, which in its early months cost them an average of £1 4s 5d a day to operate. *The Times* of 10 February commented : 'Between the pneumatic despatch and the subterranean railways, the days ought to be fast approaching when the ponderous goods vans which now fly between station and station shall disappear for ever from the streets of London.'

But the Post Office found the saving of time—the line about halved that taken by the mailcarts—useful but not vital, and refused to commit themselves in advance to use any other line the company might build. The latter, hoping that if they went ahead they would be able to convince the Post Office, the railway companies and such carriers as Pickfords and Chaplin & Horne, proceeded to build a 1¾ mile line from Euston station under Drummond Street, Hampstead Road and Tottenham Court Road to Broad Street, St Giles, where it turned sharply east to end under the company's offices at 245 Holborn, where the engines were. This tube was 4 ft 6 in wide by 4 ft high, partly in cast-iron tube and partly in brick-lined tunnel, power being provided by two horizontal engines with 24 in cylinders, three boilers, and a 22 ft diameter fan working at 150 rpm. The working air pressure and vacuum gave about 5 oz/sq in; communication was by electric telegraph.

Work had begun on 23 September 1863, and test trains were

G

first run on 10 October 1865; these did the distance in five minutes, though the working speed was reckoned at 17 mph. The cars used had a hood at one end which almost fitted the tube, the space between being sufficiently closed with projecting strips of sheet rubber. At Holborn the exit of the tube was closed by an iron door. As cars approached it, driven by atmospheric pressure, they passed the end of the exhausting main and then built up a cushion of air in front of them which served to open the door.

On 7 November a test was made for the benefit of the directors and their friends: Rammell was there, and engineers of the LNW and the Metropolitan Railway. At 245 Holborn they climbed down staircases, past steam engines and boilers, to what was then the first underground station. Some were brave enough to travel through the tube. 'The sensation at starting, and still more so upon arriving was not agreeable. For about a minute in each case there was a pressure upon the ears suggestive of diving-bell experience, a suction like that with which one is drawn under a wave, and a cold draught of wind upon the eyes, having almost the effect of falling water; but once fairly within the tube, these sensations were got rid of.' At Holborn automatic reversing was provided to a second line, meant to run to the General Post Office in Aldersgate Street and on to Pickford's depot in Gresham Street. This had, however, only been built for $\frac{3}{8}$ mile to Hatton Garden, whence it was intended to carry it over Holborn Viaduct, at that time still a project.

Then, having spent some £150,000 on their lines and experiments, the company got caught up in the crisis of 1866 that followed the failure of Overend & Gurney's bank, and could raise no more money. Experimental working on their principal line ended, and so did the service on the tube to Eversholt Street once they had given the Post Office notice to terminate it after 23 September 1866. About the end of 1868, however, it was reported that finance had been found to continue the line. It was subsequently carried on from Hatton Garden to Newgate Street and the old Post Office buildings near Cheapside, 1,658 yards from the Holborn station, and 4,738 from Euston. There were two gradients of 1 in 15 where the line dived under the Fleet valley, a section where water tended to collect, so that the mails occasionally arrived wet. In August 1872 the company, whose construction powers had expired, went on to obtain a new Act enabling them to build several lines, among them lines to St Pancras, King's Cross, and Liverpool Street stations.

The Post Office did not want to use the existing tube, but after the company's chairman had called on the Postmaster-General, they agreed that a limited quantity of mails would be carried in one direction only from 1 January 1874. The service seems to have been reliable enough, but the Post Office reckoned that, having taken into account the time lost at Euston in transporting the bags between the various platforms and the tube station, and that at Cheapside also, the tube's transit time of 17 minutes only saved them about four minutes compared to a fast horse van working from beside the train at Euston to the Post Office headquarters building. The company was itself finding difficulty in preventing excessive leakage past the cars, and had to increase their engine-power considerably : this in turn made the Post Office nervous of entrusting them with the more important and heavier mails.

In October 1874, when the Duke of Buckingham again called, this time to ask that more mails should be put on the tube, the Postmaster-General told him that there was 'no prospect whatever of the Company's system being used, at any time, for the general conveyance of the Mails between the General Post Office and Euston Station'. The company therefore gave notice to discontinue, and the service ended after 31 October 1874, the company having spent nearly £200,000. The tubes then lay derelict, though in 1895 the Post Office had them examined with the idea that they might be converted for electric traction.

Over the next thirty years many proposals for pneumatic mail-carrying tubes were made to the Post Office, including one in 1899 by the Batcheller Pneumatic Tube Company, Mr Batcheller being the inventor of the system used in the United States and

claiming to have acquired the interests of the Pneumatic Despatch Company. But the Post Office continued not to be interested in pneumatic lines, though it took a different view when
electric mail-carrying tubes became possible.

While Rammell's system was being used for parcels and postal
matter, it was developed also as the precursor of modern passenger-carrying tubes. In August 1864, an experimental single-
track line was opened in the Crystal Palace grounds, from the
Sydenham entrance to the Armoury, near the Penge gate, on
which passengers could travel between 1 and 6 p.m. for 6d
return. Nearly 600 yd long, it included curves of only 8 chains
radius and a section of 1 in 15 gradient, and was mostly laid
in a brick-lined tunnel 10 ft by 9 ft. This took a full-sized (broad
gauge) railway carriage, with sliding glass doors at each end and
seating about thirty-five passengers, round which was fitted a
diaphragm, with a fringe of bristles behind it that made a brush
to fit closely to the tunnel walls. The carriage started by gravity
from the upper end. As it entered the tunnel, two air-tight doors
shut behind it, and air was then blown in through a well in the
tunnel floor to push it forward, the journey taking about 50
seconds. Coming back, the fan was reversed, creating a vacuum
ahead of the carriage which enabled atmospheric pressure of $2\frac{1}{2}$
oz/sq in to propel it. As it got to the upper end of the tunnel,
the doors opened, and it ran by its own momentum to stop on
its brakes at the station. Power was provided by a steam engine
driving a fan of about 22 ft diameter.

As a result of this experiment in passenger-carrying, the
Waterloo & Whitehall Railway Company, with a capital of
£135,000, was authorised in 1865 to build a tube line just over
half a mile in length beneath the Thames from a station 20 ft
below Great Scotland Yard, near Whitehall, to one in York
Road, to carry passengers to and from Waterloo Station, though
extensions one way to Tottenham Court Road and the other to
the Elephant & Castle were talked of. It was originally intended
that three cars, each seating 25, should work on it, one being in
movement at any time while the other two were taking on or

setting down passengers, giving a 3 to 4 minute service, but 3-car trains were later envisaged, giving a 6 minute service. A circular brick-lined tunnel of 12 ft 9 in diameter falling at 1 in 60 would be used from Whitehall to the edge of the river (the Embankment had not then been built), and an iron tube across the Thames, falling at 1 in 26 to the centre and rising again at the same gradient to ease to 1 in 52 on its way to York Road. This iron tube would be covered outside and lined inside with brickwork and then laid in four 221 ft spans on three cylindrical brick piers in a trench dug out from the river bed, the top of the tube being 12 ft below low water level. The power station was to be at the York Road terminus, cars being pushed by a positive air pressure of 2 to 4 oz/sq in from the Waterloo end, and by similar atmospheric pressure in the other direction.

The advantages claimed in the prospectus were that the system enabled a small and therefore cheap tube to be used; trains would be noiseless and free from vibration; collisions were impossible; steep curves and gradients could be negotiated, and ventilation presented no problems.

Work began on 25 October 1865. The brick tunnel between the Whitehall terminus and the edge of the river was built, and some work done on the river section. Then, along with so many other projects, the Waterloo & Whitehall got caught up in the financial crisis of 1866. Efforts to interest the London & South Western Railway in the line failed, and work stopped after some £56,000 had been spent. Rammell, who had been paid in shares, got nothing. The company was wound up in 1882, but under London still lies the abandoned brick-lined tunnel of what might have been its first tube railway. One link the Waterloo & Whitehall had with older schemes: the iron tubes were to be built— and indeed three were wholly or partially constructed—by Messrs Samuda of Poplar.

Another offshoot of the Crystal Palace line was a proposed tube under the River Mersey. On 1 December 1865 Sir Charles Fox, a member of a firm which had enthusiastically taken up Rammell's system, and were engineers with him on the Waterloo

& Whitehall, discussed this with an influential group at Liverpool. He told them of the Sydenham experiments and of the Waterloo & Whitehall, then being built, and suggested a Mersey line 1⅜ miles long from Liverpool to Birkenhead, to cost £300,000 and yield £30,000 p.a. Each train would travel at 20 mph carrying 500 passengers at fares of 3d, 2d, and 1d. On 28 June 1866 the Mersey Pneumatic Railway Company, with a capital of £350,000, obtained an Act to build such a line from Church Street, Liverpool, to Birkenhead.

They could not have chosen a worse time, and the first directors' meeting was not held until 15 October. Given the state of the business world, no one was enthusiastic, even though Thomas Brassey junior agreed to join the board. The second did not take place until September 1871. By then another Act of 1868 had changed the company's name to the Mersey Railway Company, presumably because the failure of the Waterloo & Whitehall meant that Rammell's system was considered a handicap to raising finance. But the tunnel was not to be begun until 1879, or opened till 1886; when it was, it was steam worked.

Several overseas tubes were projected, such as one in Lausanne in 1867, and in the United States a short line was built at the American Institute Fair in September 1867 by Alfred Ely Beach of the *Scientific American*. It was 6 ft in diameter, made of wood, and carried passengers. Beach also put forward river tube projects, and a fascinating one by which letters posted in pillar boxes were automatically put aboard cars running in an underground postal tube and taken without handling to the sorting office.

He also formed the Beach Pneumatic Transit Company, which began to build a line in New York at the end of 1869. The section constructed, 312 ft long under Broadway from Warren Street to just beyond Murray Street, was a single tunnel (twin had been authorised) 9 ft in diameter that had been driven by a shield of Beach's design, the first to be used in America. Though permission to carry goods had been given, the company wanted to try passenger carrying as well. The section was opened on

26 February 1870 using an 18-passenger car and a reversible fan, but it only worked for a few months, and the company was unsuccessful in obtaining powers to build more lines. The remains of the tube, rails, shield, and car were discovered in 1912 when the subway was being built down Broadway.

Charles Bergéron, operating superintendent of a Swiss railway, and M. Berrens, French chief engineer of the Lombard-Venetian railways, both considered Rammell's system could be used to take a line over the Simplon pass. Others thought it might give us a practical Channel tunnel—but we are still waiting for that.

A hundred years later, vacuum and compressed air systems have not lost their attractions for inventors. In the 1940's, for instance, Irving Langmuir suggested a vacuum tube from New York to San Francisco within which rocket vehicles would reach speeds up to 5,000 mph; in 1965 *Life* displayed J. V. Foa of New York's plan for a car powered by turbofan jets riding in a 15 ft diameter steel tube on cushions of compressed air shot from it, to reach 400 mph; and in 1965 also, L. K. Edwards, writing in *Scientific American*, proposed 300 mph tube railways linking American cities and powered by atmospheric pressure assisted by gravity.

George Medhurst would have been delighted by all these, too.

Part Two

THE WORKING LINES

CHAPTER SEVEN

THE KINGSTOWN & DALKEY

THE winding Dalkey line was $1\frac{3}{4}$ miles long, falling for a short distance from Kingstown and then rising 71 ft mostly at a gradient of 1 in 115, but with a 400 yd section of 1 in 57 at the Dalkey end. It included three curves in half a mile, varying from 570 ft to 700 ft radius. Nearly all the 4 ft $8\frac{1}{2}$ in gauge track lay about 9 ft below ground level, in a narrow cutting which followed the alignment of the old tramroad. Wind resistance was therefore high. In addition to the tunnel there were ten bridges, only 12 ft wide and 8 ft 6 in high, giving 3 in of clearance above the train. Passengers therefore had to keep their heads inside the carriages, or lose them. Atmospheric traction was used only on the upward journey; the trains came back again by gravity.

The rails were laid on longitudinal timbers, in turn supported by cross-sleepers. The tube was 15 in diameter, laid between the rails on the cross-sleepers in 9 ft lengths 'with elastic joints, and every precaution taken to prevent its being deranged by vibration, or expansion, or contraction', as Brunel had told the Select Committee. It extended for 2,490 yd from Kingstown, the remaining 560 yd to Dalkey station being covered by the trains under their own momentum. This meant that they must leave the tube doing about 30 mph. Should the speed be insufficient, the train stopped short of the station, whereupon the third-class passengers were asked to help push, and the others walked.

At Kingstown the line ran from a platform on the southern side of the station, passengers for Dublin having to change. At Dalkey it ended in the cutting between Barnhill and Castlepark Roads, now flooded and abandoned, about half a mile north of the present station. Above it was the engine house with its tall chimney; a house called 'The Barn' now occupies the site.

The steam engine, which had been built by William Fairbairn of Manchester for the Samudas, had a huge 36 ft diameter fly-wheel, and was supplied by three Cornish boilers. It was rated at 110 hp* at 24 rpm and worked at 40 psi, the cut-off being varied automatically according to the load. The cylinder was $34\frac{1}{8}$ in diameter, with a 66 in stroke, which powered the air-pump with its $66\frac{1}{2}$ in cylinder and 66 in stroke. A gauge linked to the con-necting tube from the engine-house stood against the wall by the pump. Water was drawn from a large pond beside the engine-house, fed by a little stream that runs down from Killiney.

An engine larger than that necessary to work the Dalkey line may have been chosen to be on the 'safe side in case leakage from the valve was greater than expected, or perhaps so that it could later also work the proposed extension to Bray. In the early days there was a lot of trouble with the air-pump, due partly to the design of the outlet valve, which had greatly to be strengthened, but with consequent loss of power. Trouble also occurred with the engine, owing to the cheerful inexperience of the engineman, who seems to have been in the habit of reversing his engine without much consideration for the speed of the flywheel until Samuda came over from England and told him not to.

The tube connecting the engine-house to the main tube was 483 yd long. It was not flexibly jointed like the main tube, and, being laid on the ends of the sleepers, tended to move. A good deal of unnecessary leakage resulted. Barry Gibbons, who had become engineer to the Dublin & Kingstown company, estimated that operating costs would have been 30 per cent less if the engine and connecting tube had been better built.

When the line was opened in March 1844, trains left Kings-town every half hour between 8 a.m. and 6 p.m., soon after the

---

* Fairbairn's rated their engines by actual power developed, whereas others used a nominal power rating: by Boulton & Watt's rating this engine was $41\frac{1}{2}$ hp.

Dublin trains had got in. In 1845, however, when the Dublin & Kingstown was providing trains between 6 a.m. and 11.30 p.m. the Dalkey service was extended in the evenings to 9.30 p.m. Normal trains were light, being made up of a piston-carriage carrying third-class passengers and a composite, but at rush hours longer trains were run, and on summer weekends as many as twelve vehicles weighing about 70 tons. During the first eleven

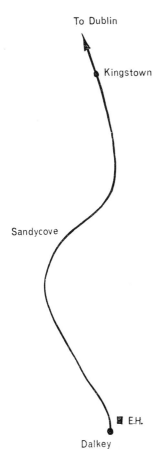

The Kingstown & Dalkey Railway

months of operation the average train weight was 17 tons, the piston assembly itself weighing one ton of this. The maximum weight of a test train that ran successfully was $74\frac{1}{2}$ tons, though it did not quite reach Dalkey station; one of almost 79 tons failed on the sharpest curve.

On short trains one brakesman beside the driver was carried. With four or five coach trains, there was a second, and on longer trains three; these acted also as guards, and at the stations as porters. The braking seems to have been quite efficient. On tests, a 40 ton train was stopped from 26 mph in 176 yd; another, weight not given, from 36 mph in 198 yd. In both cases the stops were made with the piston in the tube.

During this time the average speed of trains was $26\frac{1}{3}$ mph, start to stop. The working rule was not to do the journey in less than four minutes, though trains could do it under three, and sometimes did. The maximum speed obtained during tests was $51\frac{1}{2}$ mph which, considering the curves, everyone considered was quite fast enough, in spite of the banking and the guard-rails. It involved a 30 ton train leaving the end of the tube at 42 mph, and pulling up in a quarter of a mile. Thoughtfully, no buffer-stops were provided at the Dalkey end, and occasionally a train went right through the station and off the rails without coming to any great harm. Trains returned more sedately to Kingstown, by gravity at an average of about 18 mph.

There were two spectacular runs in the early days. A train was standing in Kingstown station when the driver, thinking that the coupling between the piston carriage and the next coach was not properly fastened, got down to see to it. At that moment his carriage began to move. He jumped back on to it, and together they shot off at a speed estimated as over 60 mph before he could apply the brake. It must have been quite exciting. In the second case, given by Dr T. R. Robinson to the 1845 Select Committee, a student, F. Elrington, was with the driver and one or two other men, when the piston carriage got away. Even if we discount Dr Robinson's suggested *average* speed of 84 mph the trip probably set up a temporary world record.

At Kingstown, when the Dublin train was nearly due, that to Dalkey was pushed forward by hand down the slight slope until the piston entered the short length of tube behind the closed entrance valve, where it was held on the brake. Five minutes were allowed for passengers to change trains. Because there was at first no telegraph between the station and the engine-house at Dalkey, the engineman was instructed to start pumping just before departure time, the exact time varying slightly according to the weight of the train. As soon as the gauge in the piston-carriage or at the mouth of the tunnel at the end of the platform showed the driver that he had sufficient vacuum, he gave the signal to open the valve, released his brake, and the train started.

Working vacuum was about 15 or 16 in of mercury (though half that would move a light train) and could be obtained with about 45 seconds of pumping. A very heavy train of nine or ten coaches might need three minutes or more, and a vacuum nearer the practical maximum of $27\frac{1}{2}$ in. To these times of pumping must be added the running time of four minutes. As the look-out man at Dalkey engine-house saw the train appear, he told the engineman to shut off steam. In the first eleven months the engine pumped $117\frac{1}{2}$ double strokes for each train—that is, about 5·2 minutes of pumping at $22\frac{1}{2}$ strokes to the minute. The rest of the time it was idle.

At Dalkey the train had passed beyond the end of the tube, and was held in the station on the brake. The piston was swung sideways to be clear of the tube and secured, and the train was ready for its return journey. At departure time, the brake was released, and it started down the 1 in 57, and ran by gravity to Kingstown, unless by chance there was enough head wind to cause it to stop in the approach tunnel.

In the same eleven months, 17,506 trains had been run, half of which were atmospherically propelled and half run by gravity, averaging $3\frac{1}{3}$ coaches to a train and 4 passengers to a coach. The line worked on 337 days, and was stopped on $8\frac{1}{2}$ days, 7 because of breakages in the steam engine, $1\frac{1}{2}$ because of a slip on the line. Valve trouble in cold weather caused the cancellation of a few trains, but no serious break in service.

When Robert Nicholson, engineer of the Newcastle & North Shields Railway, visited the line about the beginning of 1845, he noted the staff employed on the line : two enginemen, two stokers and a lookout boy at the engine-house, for two shifts were worked, except apparently by the boy; three maintenance men for looking after the continuous valve; a member of the station staff at Kingstown to operate the entrance valve, and another at Dalkey to work the shut-off valve at the other end of the tube; on the train the driver and brakesman. As the railway settled down, however, one valveman (as the maintenance men were called) proved enough, and the station staff must have had other jobs also.

The accounts for the year ended 28 February 1847, the third of operation, showed these expenses :

Engine and pump	£	£
Coal	695	
Enginemen's and stokers' wages	361	
Oil, tallow, waste	124	
Mechanics' wages for repairs ...	385	
Materials for repairs	367	
Other expenses	93	
	——	2,025
Main tube and piston		
Materials for repairs	741	
Mechanics' wages—repairs ...	129	
Valveman	60	
	——	930
		£2,955

After its first exciting year, men lost interest in the Dalkey line, concentrating instead on the London & Croydon, the South Devon, and the many atmospheric projects of 1845 and 1846, though in September 1847 the Viceroy visited it, being shown round by James Pim. Yet it worked satisfactorily until 1854. To begin with, it made a small profit; later it did not, partly because the novelty had worn off, but it brought enough extra fares to the Dublin line for it to be well worth keeping, and helped to develop residential growth round Dalkey for the future benefit of the Dublin & Kingstown.

For the convenience of residents in east Kingstown and Glastule, Samuda suggested a means of operating short-distance services from Kingstown station to the Bullock Road crossing. A carriage for the intermediate station would be attached to each Dalkey-bound train, and slipped at Bullock Road. For the return journey it would use a separate 9 in atmospheric tube. This tube was actually supplied, but never laid down, for Samuda had changed his mind. He now planned a large spring, to be connected to the carriage-axle by a clutch. On the way from Kingstown the spring, being put in gear, would be wound up. The carriage having been detached at Bullock Road, would be held there by its brake until it was ready to start. Then the brake

Coombe Cellars Haccombe

Commyn's Summer House Engine House

Electric Telegraph

XIII. *The South Devon Railway in 1848: (above) the estuary of the Teign, with the summer house in the foreground, and the engine-house, named after it, behind; (below) Newton station and engine-house*

Tank and Engine House

Newton Station

Road to Newton

West face of the Dainton Tunnel

Engine House and Coal Siding

Dartington

Weir on the River Dart

xiv. *The South Devon Railway in 1848: (above) Dainton tunnel and engine-house, with the coal siding in front; (below) laying the last few tubes up to the Dart bridge at Totnes*

would be released, and the spring would give the vehicle a push off which, with the help of gravity, would take it to Kingstown. But though Samuda paid for at any rate some of the material he supplied, no intermediate station was built, or short-distance service worked, on the atmospheric line. After its conversion to steam, Kingstown Sandycove station was provided at Bullock Road, all trains having to stop there to prevent excessive speed in either direction.

In 1845 an extension for $5\frac{1}{4}$ miles from Dalkey to Bray was promoted at an estimated cost of £80,000. It was to be built by a nominally separate company, the Kingstown & Bray, to which the Dalkey line was to be transferred. The extension was to be constructed on a reverse slope, so that it also could be worked one way by gravity, a single engine-house at the summit being able to exhaust the tube for trains climbing either slope. In this year Pim issued £25,000 of 4 per cent debentures to repay the Dalkey loan to the Board of Works, so getting rid of the obligation annually to repay a portion of the principal. The future looked so good that the happy shareholders of the Dublin & Kingstown voted him a present of £1,000.

Negotiations took place with the Great Western Railway for a further extension to Wexford and Waterford; Brunel surveyed it, but nothing happened, and the Kingstown & Bray bill failed on standing orders. In 1846 the Dublin & Kingstown decided themselves to build the Bray extension, though by now there was little probability that it would have been atmospheric. They bought up the outstanding Kingstown & Bray scrip for £27,500 and got their Act in 1846. Simultaneously they consented to lease their rights to the Waterford, Wexford, Wicklow & Dublin Railway, who with their agreement had been authorised, also in 1846, to build a line to Dublin. The WWWD having failed to progress, the Dublin & Kingstown tried to recover powers to make the Bray extension, but were refused. The WWWD became the Dublin & Wicklow, and set about raising capital; the Dalkey stayed as it was.

About the end of 1845 the longitudinal valve was completely

H

renewed at the cost of £867, the company reporting that it should now last for four years. In 1848 fares on the Dalkey were halved, and in October the company reported that receipts had increased. At this time the Dalkey was costing 1s 3d per train mile, against 2s 4½d on the Dublin & Kingstown; the two figures are hardly comparable, but the cost of the atmospheric line was certainly not excessive; in 1849 it was given as 1s 8¼d against 3s. Then, on 24 November, the air-pump fractured badly and stopped working. Hurriedly the company converted *Princess*, the first locomotive to be built in Ireland. Her chimney was cut down, a shelter built over the footplate, and from 23 December 1848 to 4 February 1849 she coped with the light winter trains, pulling three coaches and taking six minutes. Then atmospheric working began again, on Whit-Monday the trains carrying 6,068 passengers.

Powers had been obtained to lease the Dublin–Kingstown line to the WWWD. But the latter, having failed to raise capital for its full scheme, curtailed it, and decided to build a line to Wicklow only. Its name was changed, capital was found, and work began on a railway from Dublin through Dundrum to Bray, with a branch from Bray to Dalkey. These lines were brought into use on 10 July 1854. Before that, on the evening of Wednesday 12 April, the last atmospheric train had run, the section being then handed over to the Dublin & Wicklow, who for a time substituted an omnibus service. The Dalkey line was then converted to the standard Irish 5 ft 3 in gauge, the curves being eased, the track lowered to save raising bridges, and the narrow Dalkey coaches being fitted with wide footboards. On 11 October 1855 the Bray–Kingstown section was reopened, steam-worked, but on 20 March 1856 was again closed for further improvements. These made, the Dublin & Kingstown directors no longer objected to leasing their line, and on 1 July the lease came into force at a rent which gave the shareholders 9½ per cent on their original capital; on the 2nd the line reopened. Soon afterwards the Dublin & Kingstown itself was also converted to the 5ft 3 in gauge.

So, after ten years of public working, atmospheric traction ended on the Dalkey. Though not cheap to maintain, the line was probably more economically worked in that way than by steam, and its ending came as part of a process of gauge conversion and rebuilding, and not of any failure of the system. Engineers had come from far and wide to see it, admire it, experiment with it, and for a time the name Dalkey had attained a European fame on the strength of a pump, a tube and a piston. Now they were gone, and only in France did Clegg and Samuda still have a working memorial.

CHAPTER EIGHT

THE CROYDON LINES

E ARLY in August 1844 the London & Croydon Railway was authorised to build a third track for atmospheric trains on the east side of its existing lines from Corbett's Lane, junction with the London & Greenwich, to Jolly Sailor, junction for the Brighton line; from there to Croydon one of the existing two lines would be converted to atmospheric. Together with the extension to Epsom, the company contemplated about twenty miles of tube.

A few days earlier, the board had agreed to the outcome of their engineer's negotiations with the London & Greenwich whereby that company agreed to reduce their tolls if the Croydon would run at least as many Croydon and Epsom trains to London Bridge as to the Bricklayers Arms at fares no higher, the Croydon in turn consenting to pay £25,000 towards the cost of an additional Greenwich line for atmospheric trains for the $1\frac{3}{4}$ miles between London Bridge and Corbett's Lane, and to lend what further money might be needed for it. Fares were at once reduced, and on 25 July trains began to run to London Bridge. After 31 March 1845 the Croydon ran no more to Bricklayers Arms: by then the Greenwich had been since the first of January the property of the South Eastern.

Cubitt now appointed Charles Hutton Gregory as assistant engineer for the atmospheric lines and started with the five-mile section from Croydon to Dartmouth Arms,* with intermediate stations at Sydenham, Anerley, and Jolly Sailor. The tube was in two sections, three miles from Forest Hill to Norwood, and

* On 3 July 1845 the name was changed to Forest Hill, Jolly Sailor being also changed to Norwood.

two miles thence to Croydon. An order went to Maudslay, Son & Field for three (increased to four) pairs of engines, to Samuda Bros for the continuous valve and its fastenings ready fixed to the tubes, at £15 per chain, and to the Coalbrookdale company for the 15 in tubes, at £7 10s a ton including carriage to the Thames wharf, deliveries to begin in December.

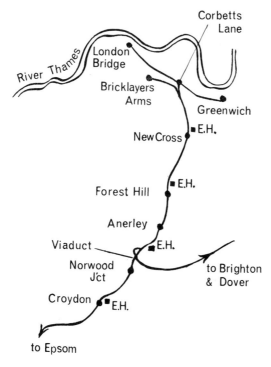

The London & Croydon Railway

The extension was delayed for want of plans on which negotiations for land purchase could be started, but on 17 October the ground was broken for the Croydon line, and thereafter the earthworks and the necessary station alterations went steadily on. In January 1845 Cubitt approved the design for the timber viaduct that was to carry the atmospheric track at 1 in 50 gradients over the Brighton & Dover lines at Norwood, and its construction started. But by 20 February no tubes had arrived. When they did the proportion of breakages was high. The Coalbrookdale company explained that in spite of having shipped them by tramroad to the head of the Shropshire Canal, thence by 5 ton tub-boats to the Birmingham & Liverpool Junction Canal to be put on 20 ton narrow boats to Brentford for transhipment again to river barges, they had had few breakages. They blamed the company's unloading, and criticised the design. The company replied blaming their manufacture.

In mid-March 1845 earthworks were reported nearly finished, and rails and sleepers on the ground. In May James Pearson was appointed to superintend the working and repair of the stationary engines, and was sent to Dalkey and Manchester to study them, but in June, though the engine-houses at Croydon, Norwood, and Forest Hill were ready, the engines had not been delivered. In July the company decided that the Epsom extension should be double-tracked, and minuted to consult Cubitt upon the expediency of doubling their own as well. No change was made—things might have been very different if there had been. Writing about this time of engine-house design, a newspaper informed its readers that 'it has been determined by the architects of the Croydon and Epsom line to give their chimneys an architectural character, and to relieve their baldness by the addition of proportions and decorations which have hitherto belonged almost exclusively to the bell-towers of the early Gothic churches. And . . . to construct the station and engine-houses in the style of half-timbered manor houses of the Middle Ages.'

The engines, delivered late, were installed and fitted up from July onwards, on 21 August the tube was cleared, and on the 22nd the first tests were held, using one Norwood engine only. Samuda was delighted, for 'the Brighton train of 7 carriages pulled by two Engines passed us at full speed while we were at rest at the Dartmouth Arms station. We started one minute after they passed, and overhaul'd them at the Wood Viaduct where our line passes over theirs . . . we were going upwards of 60 miles per hour when we passed them.' On further tests early in

September speeds of 70 mph were reached with six carriages, and 30 mph with sixteen, but a labourer had stepped on to the line as a train was passing. He was Michael Murphy, and the company paid for his funeral.

Samuda told a shareholders' meeting on 9 September: 'some slight delays have arisen from the improvements in and novelty of many of the parts introduced in this, the first single line of railway, which works both ways on the atmospheric principle, rendering additions and variations necessary'. However, 'it only remains to complete the station arrangements, get the engines into proper working order, and instruct and practise the tele-graph men, enginemen and train conductors, in their respective duties, to enable it to be opened for public traffic'. Afterwards the shareholders were taken by special steam train to Croydon, then by a six-coach atmospheric train to Forest Hill, averaging 30 mph and with a maximum speed of 45, and back to Croydon the same way.

On Monday 20 October the directors invited a large party of ladies and gentlemen to gather for a cold collation at London Bridge. Afterwards, at 2 p.m. they were taken by special train to Forest Hill, where a piston carriage was substituted for the loco-motive, and the train then covered the five miles to Croydon in $8\frac{3}{4}$ minutes. This trip was reported in the *Illustrated London News* as follows:

At nine minutes before two, the train, drawn by a locomotive, left the London station, arriving at the Dartmouth Arms . . . in eleven minutes. At seven minutes and a half past two, the train again left its point of rest, and at eight minutes and three-quarters past two, the piston got into the pipe, and proceeded at a rapid rate. Within a minute, a speed of 12 miles an hour was attained; in the second minute, 18 miles an hour; in the third minute 25 miles; in the fourth minute, 34 miles; in the fifth, 40 miles; and in the sixth minute it reached its maximum speed, which was about 52 miles an hour, at which it continued till it slackened speed on approaching the Croydon terminus. . . . The train [had] ten carriages, which with passengers, exceeded fifty tons. The barometer in the piston carriage indicated a pressure of between

25 and 26. The party, having inspected the machinery, left Croydon at a minute and a half before three. . . . The travelling was
tolerably easy during the greater part of the journey, but at
intervals the oscillation was perfectly frightful. On their return,
most of the party occupied first-class carriages. The movement
of the train was scarcely felt. . . . Another experimental trip took
place on this line on Tuesday. . . . The oscillation in the third-
class carriages was not so observable as on the previous day.

A selected few finished up with dinner at the London Tavern
in Bishopsgate Street. On the following days further runs took
place, with speeds of up to 75 mph reported.

A fortnight later the London & Croydon company announced
that it had agreed to amalgamate with the London & Brighton.
On 8 November, a Croydon shareholders' meeting heard their
chairman say that they deserved great credit for their atmospheric
experiments: 'he had not the least doubt that ere long the atmospheric principle would effect as great a revolution in the present
system of railways as did the discovery of the force and power of
steam effect in the former mode of travelling'. He added that
the proposed Great Kent line would not be affected by the amalgamation, as it was almost independent, and that the success
of the experiments would probably help the Direct Portsmouth
Line through Parliament, especially if there could be an arrangement with the LSW.

But behind the scenes a battle went on between the two groups
of directors over the Portsmouth line, those of the Brighton trying to conceal an agreement with the LSW that would have
involved dropping atmospheric traction, the Croydon directors
complaining that access to essential information was being refused. They were fewer and less powerful, and shareholders'
opinions tended to be against them. In December a Croydon
shareholder wrote to the Press: 'Let Mr Wilkinson see that we
will not sacrifice our interest to his Ass-most-pheric schemes', and
one at the Brighton's meeting protested that 'all the expense of
the trials which are now making on the Croydon Atmospheric
Railway, for which no satisfactory result is deduced, will by the

amalgamation which is now taking place be saddled in part upon us'.

Meanwhile, work went on. Each engine-house was to have two 50 hp low-pressure beam engines with 40 in cylinders, which could be run separately or linked together, and a third small one for pumping water. Forest Hill, to be the main passing station, was to have two more to speed up the crossing of trains and help work the incline, but these were not installed until much later. There would be a fifth pair at New Cross, and a sixth in an engine-house at London Bridge. When the first tests were made, the engines worked well enough, though there had been trouble in starting them, and the breaking of a crankshaft at Forest Hill on 17 December was to be a portent. But Samuda disliked them, and in September tried to get hold of a pair for New Cross that G. & J. Rennie had built for the South Devon Railway. They could not be released, the board turned down Rennie's quotation for a similar pair as too expensive, and it seems that Maudslay's supplied a pair for New Cross after all, to be used until they could be replaced by others from Boulton & Watt. The company's Act stipulated that smoke must not be made. They intended to burn anthracite, but started operations with coke. Judging by complaints they received, they later burned coal.

The Company's architect was W. H. Breakspear, though the detail of the engine-houses was by Raphael Brandon who only got £30 for his designs, including the cost of lithographing them. What was saved on him, however, was spent on construction : Cubitt gloomily told the Select Committee that the buildings for the line 'are very ornamental, and will cost a great deal of money. Of course, that is a matter of taste.' In two respects the design failed : almost as soon as the line opened for traffic Grissell & Peto, the contractors who had built them, were asked to take down 'the conical spire of the Norwood Engine House'; generally also the engine foundations were not strong enough to take the weight, and had to be strengthened with brickwork and bearing girders.

It was convenient for the enginemen to live near their work, and during 1846 cottages were built for them at Forest Hill. Each engine-house had a siding for coal trucks, and Norwood a crane worked by atmospheric power to unload it to internal coal cellars. Water was run into internal tanks, at Forest Hill from the old Croydon Canal, elsewhere probably from wells. The engine-houses were connected by Cooke & Wheatstone electric telegraph; judging by the absence of minuted complaints, it worked well.

Problems still had to be solved. One was to prevent atmospheric trains mowing down passengers off the locomotive-hauled trains. The atmospheric line had been laid outside the existing track, and only six feet away. It was fenced, but at some stations passengers off the steam trains had to cross the atmospheric track to leave the station. Gregory decided the safest way to get them off was by a drawbridge which would normally be kept raised, but would be lowered by station staff when necessary. The silence of the new service, however, led to some narrow escapes. During the first trials an atmospheric train arrived at one station while passengers from a steam train were still on the platform, and four men only just got the bridge up in time. A few months later a 'police constable' from Anerley was before the board after a similar narrow escape. Another problem resulted from the tube having been laid low between the rails. When Cubitt wished to switch the atmospheric train on to the steam track to bring it alongside the station at Forest Hill, he had to prevent the piston fouling the running rails. He therefore designed complicated and expensive points which moved not only the tongues of the rails, but also those rail sections that lay between the track taken by the piston carriage.

To avoid a clash between Samuda and Gregory, it had been decided in September to install Henry Hensman, one of Samuda's men, as atmospheric manager. Soon afterwards Gregory resigned, going as engineer to the Bristol & Exeter, and was replaced for 'general superintendence' by Joseph Cubitt, the engineer's son, with three assistants, C. B. Child on the atmospheric line, Henry Colson on the old Croydon, and Henry Carr on the Epsom extension.

By the end of October Hensman reported that at least four atmospheric test trains every weekday were running between Croydon and Forest Hill 'with perfect facility', and the company gave notice to the Board of Trade that they were ready to open. Permission was reported on 11 November. The earthwork for the third line was now almost finished to New Cross. Samuda therefore told the board that the 'atmospheric apparatus is all prepared' for completion into London, and that all now waited for the Greenwich widening, without which there would have to be a change of power at Corbett's Lane, with inconvenience to the public and loss of profit to the company. A letter was therefore written to the South Eastern to hurry them up.

However, the engines were not all ready, and Samuda and others concerned wanted to continue testing while the third line was also used by steam trains. Eventually, after the carriage works had reported that three piston and two heater carriages were at work, with another two of the former and one of the latter almost ready, Cubitt wrote to the board at its meeting on 1 January 1846. 'I am ill at ease about your "Atmospheric" proceedings. Some time since, I had an idea that it would be well, and politic and economical, even to complete the thing to New Cross Station before opening to the Public to carry the Croydon Traffic, but subsequent events have tended to change, or at all events to modify, that opinion.' He went on to say that the good name both of the railway and the system would suffer if public opening were longer delayed. There should be an end to experiments. 'I feel a sort of "Pressure from without", which though indefinable intimates plainly enough that the atmospheric must now begin to stand upon its own merits, and no longer upon promise and assertions.' Locomotives and piston carriages could be changed easily enough at Forest Hill without affecting the current timetable, and he therefore recommended that as soon as arrangements could be made, they should '*quietly* put the Croydon Traffic on the atmospheric line'.

The company agreed, refused permission to Robert Stephenson and G. P. Bidder to make some experiments on the grounds that their hostility was well known, and they could study the line working like everyone else, told the carriage works to hurry up and complete the six piston and six heater carriages that were needed, and opened the line on 19 January. But not for long. About 11 a.m. the crankshaft of one of the pumping engines at Croydon broke; after the engine had been uncoupled traffic was worked with the other until 7.20 p.m., when that also broke, and for the next two days the trains were steam-hauled; atmospheric working began again on the 22nd, by which time wrought-iron instead of cast-iron shafts had been fitted to the Croydon engines. The directors were very angry, and wrote to Maudslay's to express the 'deep mortification of the Board' at these failures on opening day; they were the fifth of their kind, and the engineers were told to provide duplicates of certain parts.

Over the next fortnight there was a good deal of trouble with the engines; breakages of connecting rods, failures of the pump valves, and the difficulty of disconnecting the coupled engines when one went wrong. The track seems also to have added to the Croydon's commuters' troubles while they were being used as guinea-pigs, perhaps because of Cubitt's involved points. Here is the record of five early days:

Sunday 1 February

    10.05 a.m. ran into the buffers at Croydon.

    8.20 p.m. up, detained at the viaduct for want of vacuum and taken to Forest Hill by loco. After working for the day, one of the pistons was damaged because some of the points were not set quite right.

Monday 2 February

    8.05 a.m. down, late at Croydon.

    8.20 p.m. up, stopped for want of vacuum. Later went on.

Tuesday 3 February

    8.05 a.m. piston carriage and three coaches off the rails—points wrong. Piston and wheel damaged.

Wednesday 4 February
> Piston carriage off the rails at the siding at Croydon. Bad state of the rails.

Thursday 5 February
> 8.05 a.m. worked by loco—not enough vacuum. Piston carriage off the track at Forest Hill—bad rails.

One feels that the 8.05 was a train to avoid.

Samuda protested to the board in a long letter and orally. He had not been consulted about the Maudslay engines and equipment, although he was an engine maker and had obtained that used at Dalkey. Too many parts were of cast iron (at some time every crankshaft of every engine broke), and in any case the engines lacked the power to work the air-pumps sufficiently when these were under their greatest load. As for the air-pump valves, Field of Maudslay's had suggested substituting very light wooden valves for the large, flat, iron ones used at Dalkey, but Field's were too delicate to stand up to sudden variations in load, while their lightness caused them to get gummed up by small pieces of the composition from the tube sucked into the pumps, and would have to be replaced by stronger ones of the Dalkey type. He asked for complete control under Cubitt of the engines and track, and said: 'unless I am allowed to make such alterations as I have for months past described as imperative, I can see no respite from the repeated interruptions and the unceasing anxiety I have had to encounter while struggling on with these Engines as at present constructed'.

Cubitt agreed, and so did the board. Samuda should be given sole charge; parts should be replaced, and duplicates ordered; alterations should be made in the design of the engine and pumps. It looks also as if the derailments had something to do with driving as well as track, for the Board minuted 'That the Stokers and other men be appointed instead of the Guards, as Drivers of the atmospheric Trains', at 25s rising to 30s p.w.

In the *Railway Times* of 21 February 1846 appeared a letter: 'I have recently been informed by an acquaintance who makes frequent use of the Croydon railway, that since the atmospheric line has been opened to the public for regular traffic (I believe about three weeks ago) it has been stopped for two days at least by the breaking of the engines, that there have been since occasional stoppages from unexplained causes; the trains have had to be taken by the locomotives; that not infrequently the train overshoots the stations, and as it cannot be pushed back, the passengers have had at some inconvenience to walk back along the line to the stations; also that the consumption of fuel by the stationary engines is so great, that at one station alone it would about suffice for the working of the whole line by locomotive power. . . . If there be really these disadvantages after what we have been led to expect, and after so long a time in preparation to make the machine work perfectly, it is to be hoped that the Directors will have the candour to admit their error, and not put us to needless further expense in obstinately pursuing an extension of the Atmospheric line.'

But now things began to go better. On 5 March a new time-table was introduced with 32 trains a day, which included non-stop runs between Forest Hill and Croydon, and the company felt confident enough to send every MP and peer a free pass to travel for three months on Saturdays in a non-stop train from Croydon to Forest Hill and back. The timetable included a first-class only at 9.45 a.m. from Croydon to London Bridge with one stop to change traction at Forest Hill; it returned at 4.50 p.m. However, the South Eastern had taken no steps to make the extra Greenwich line, and the company began to wonder how best to compel them.

April was fairly uneventful except when the beam of one of the Forest Hill engines broke and shifted part of the engine-house wall. In May it was reported that the track from Forest Hill to New Cross would be ready for traffic in June, though the second pair of Forest Hill engines were not ready or likely to be. Neither could engines yet be obtained for New Cross. Meanwhile those at Croydon had been fitted with Stanley's smoke-consuming apparatus, which did not help Mr Peacock of Norwood, who lived near the engine-house. He repeatedly complained of the noise and smoke, and the hot and filthy smell of the water from it which drained into a section of the old canal that he owned and poisoned his fish.

In May the timetable was again improved, to show 19 trains a day from London and 20 from Croydon. Of the London departures, three stopped at Forest Hill only to change the traction, one at Sydenham and Forest Hill, the others at all stations, except one not stopping at Anerley and one at Norwood. Of the up trains, four stopped only at Forest Hill, one at Sydenham and Forest Hill, the rest at all stations. The Sunday service showed 18 trains each way, five stopping at New Cross, Forest Hill and Anerley only, the others at all stations. First, second and third class carriages ran on all trains: a return of rolling stock made to the Board of Trade showed the Croydon company to possess six piston and four heater carriages, and 12 first, 12 second, 2 composite first and second, and 19 third-class coaches.

The *Railway Record*, which was sympathetic to atmospheric traction, made a check on the running during the week ended 9 May. They reported that of the stopping trains the 20 up took an average of 15·4 minutes, and the 19 down 17 minutes, against the 15 of the timetable; the fast trains took 8·2 minutes up and 9·2 minutes down against a scheduled 7 minutes. They added some interesting figures for the London & Croydon generally, and described the railway as charging less than any other in the kingdom :

Date	Passengers Carried 1–14 May inc.	Receipts £	Fares		
			1st s d	2nd s d	3rd s d
1843	8,680	547	2 3	1 9	– –
1844	22,293	908	2 3	1 0	none till July
1845	33,069	1,222	1 3	1 0	9
1846	42,365	1,462	1 3	1 0	9

The increasing traffic was gratifying. The chairman now talked of soon laying a double atmospheric line, but Samuda was having difficulty in getting heavy trains over the viaduct if stationary engine trouble prevented them getting a run at it. He decided to put a capstan powered from the tube at the highest point, so that they could be rope-assisted.

Up till now it had been assumed that atmospheric traction would be used on the Epsom extension, for which stations were planned at Carshalton, Sutton, Cheam, Ewell, and Epsom. In the previous December an extension of the Coalbrookdale contract for tubes had been agreed (though maybe not acted upon). In January it had been intended to give the engine contract to Maudslay's, but the Board's annoyance with that firm caused them also to seek tenders elsewhere for the engines in two sizes, with 36 in cylinders, and with those of 45 in for the proposed double pumping station at Carshalton. Prices per pair of engines varied spectacularly:

	36 in £	45 in £
Maudslay, Son & Field ...	9,900	15,400
G. & J. Rennie	8,310	12,992
J. & A. Blyth	7,000	11,750
Boulton & Watt	4,950	8,300

Engines were therefore ordered from Boulton & Watt.

In February the Clerk to the Course at Epsom wrote to suggest a subscription by the company towards a race to be called the 'Epsom Atmospheric Railway Stakes', and was told it would be considered when the line reached Epsom. In March Grissell & Peto wrote that 'presuming the ornamental Engine Houses on the atmospheric line have met the approbation of the Directors', they would be happy to build those beyond Croydon, and were told specifications were not ready. In May, however, a sub-committee started to examine Samuda's plans for engine-houses for the extension before seeking tenders, and in June Samuda delivered a quantity of valve material for the Epsom line.

He chose a bad moment. By early May valve leakage was showing itself, and towards its end the line had to be taken out of use. The main cause was a new pattern of valve. On the Dalkey

xv. *Two views of Starcross engine-house: (above) from the ferry pier, and (below) looking up the line from below the pier*

XVI. *(above) Exeter engine-house converted for gas-making; (below) Starcross engine-house in use as a chapel*

this had consisted of a strip of leather riveted to a second one the width of the iron plates above it. Rubbing occurred between the outer iron plates and the leather, and the leather hinge itself tended to tear when the valve was pushed upwards. Samuda therefore substituted for the upper thickness of leather thin plates

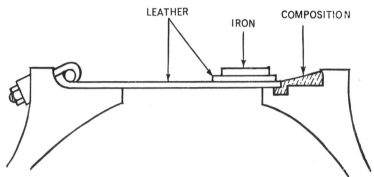

Drawing made by Samuda in November 1846 of the double leather valve then fitted on the Croydon line. Note that neither the upper leather nor the iron plate above it runs the full width of the slot. He emphasized that the composition should be sloped back as shown to give greater adhesion to the iron of the tube

of steel about four inches long. He hoped these would protect the leather and at the same time prove springy enough to allow the valve to rise without straining the hinge.

But the steel plates did not survive daily operation. Many broke off, leaving a sharp edge which cut the leather every time the valve lifted, and sometimes severed it. Leakage and loss of power followed. A secondary difficulty was the sealing composition, which did not resist some very hot weather which occurred that summer, a temperature of 130° over the valve being once recorded. A double-leather valve had therefore to be fitted throughout, and a new sealing composition invented and applied. This took about six weeks, the line reopening on 13 July. Meanwhile all traffic had to be worked over the two locomotive lines, much to the annoyance of the London & Brighton, who complained of many delays to their trains.

The most balanced comment perhaps came from the *Railway*

I

Chronicle : 'All that we gather, so far, from the history of the Croydon trial, is—not that the invention is a failure—but that it is still a long way within the first experimental stage. As this experiment will consist, for real use, of two—to arrive, namely, first at a service that may be trusted, and then at the financial results of the system; we should be glad to see the former more advanced than it is, in order that some progress might be made in the second and more practically important inquiry.' In spite of all the troubles, however, the London & Croydon carried in the five months February–June 1846 a monthly average of 81,642 passengers, whereas for the six months February–July 1845 the average had been 65,578; an increase of over 24 per cent.

Cubitt reacted to Samuda's hurried and tactless delivery of nearly £10,000 worth of valves and fastenings for the Epsom line by saying that 'after what had passed, I feel loath to certify anything Atmospheric beyond Croydon'. In a report to a board meeting on 1 July, he wrote that he was not yet satisfied that the atmospheric system had commercial value or certainty of action, and wanted no extension until he was. Meanwhile there was the problem of working the growing traffic. The first essential was to find out definitely whether a vacuum of 18–20 in could be reliably got to work 45 ton half-hour trains. If not, the 'mechanical construction and arrangement of the pipe and longitudinal valve are too imperfect to be worthy of more extended application'. Without reliability, he was not prepared to increase power either by doubling the line or putting in a larger tube, 'although the present apparatus is confessedly unequal to the traffic'. He added that the New Cross section should be got to work as soon as possible—'much depends on the mode which the Atmospheric shall act upon it'.

So on the one hand rails for the Epsom line were bought on the assumption of locomotive working, and a decision taken to lay a third line from Norwood Junction to Croydon to give a double locomotive track throughout, in view of the expected traffic from Epsom and Portsmouth; on the other a design by Raphael Brandon for the New Cross engine and boiler houses was chosen, and soon afterwards a tender accepted; it was agreed to move the existing tracks near Corbett's Lane to enable the atmospheric line to be extended, and the company's solicitors were told to enforce the construction of the new Greenwich line by the South Eastern.

In the week ending 25 July, when 26,000 passengers were carried, the *Railway Record* checked the running of some consecutive trains:

Trains	Carriages	Weight Tons	Av. speed start to stop mph	Max. speed mph	Vacuum
9.30 a.m. up express	6	35	$34\frac{1}{2}$	$56\frac{1}{4}$	$12\frac{1}{2}$–$19\frac{1}{2}$
10.15 a.m. down stopping	8	50	17	30	19 –$13\frac{3}{4}$
10.50 a.m. up express	4	22	43	64·28	19 – $8\frac{1}{2}$

On another day of the week they noted the 9.15 up, with 9 carriages weighing 55 tons, and crowded, took the gradient over the viaduct at $28\frac{1}{4}$ mph with $18\frac{1}{2}$–22 in vacuum. A note on the operating vacuums shows that most working was within the range of 17 to 24 in, much of it at 20 and over. On two quoted occasions the piston entered the tube within two minutes of the arrival of the train in the opposite direction, which shows that the valve must have been in excellent condition after its renewal. In early August the *Railway Times* reported that 'a very sensible improvement has taken place in the working of this line since the introduction of the new composition to the valve'. A letter Samuda wrote to Bergin of the Dalkey on 17 November shows him well satisfied with the new composition: 'We have never had a piece however small either thrown out of the groove or drawn into the pipe, & instead of 15 men, the number we were obliged to put on the 5 miles last year when the cold weather first set in, we have but 4 on the whole length & they have literally nothing more to do than see that all is right. I am sure you will do your work far better with only *one* man than now with three . . . we have had the ice over the composition on one exposed part of the line, but it was quite as soft and seal'd quite as well as at 100.' But it was not to perform perfectly in the frosts of the following February.

The tube had now been laid to New Cross, and the engines were being erected there. Beyond to Corbett's Lane the line was ready for the tube to be laid, and Wilkinson was reported as saying that the line would be completed to London Bridge as soon as arrangements then pending with the SER were adjusted.

Tests, perhaps to impress the London & Brighton, were run on 11 August, when a piston carriage and three coaches reached 75 mph over a quarter mile, and ran at exactly 60 mph for $1\frac{1}{4}$ miles. Then the *Railway Record* did some detailed observing, from which the following record of part of a day's running is taken:

Tuesday 18 August 1846

Train	Carriages	Weight Tons	Maximum Speed mph	Time Allowed min	Time Taken min & sec
8.00 up	8	52	$35\frac{1}{4}$	15	17.16
8.15 down	8	44	36	18	15.20
8.50 up	7	$45\frac{1}{2}$	$51\frac{1}{4}$	10	10.40
9.15 down	8	44	45	18	14.11
9.50 up	7	$45\frac{1}{2}$	$54\frac{1}{2}$	8	8.15
10.15 down	8	44	$40\frac{3}{4}$	18	14.53
10.50 up	4	26	60	8	7.50
11.15 down	9	50	39	18	18.37
12.15 up	8	44	$35\frac{1}{4}$	15	15.18
12.15 down	8	44	39	18	$16.19\frac{1}{2}$
1.15 up	8	44	$38\frac{1}{4}$	15	$16.20\frac{1}{2}$
1.15 down	7	$38\frac{1}{2}$	$33\frac{3}{4}$	18	$18.33\frac{3}{4}$
2.15 up	7	$38\frac{1}{2}$	$36\frac{1}{2}$	15	$15.32\frac{3}{4}$
2.45 down	4	$22\frac{1}{2}$	46	10	$8.44\frac{3}{4}$
3.15 up	8	44	36	15	$16.03\frac{1}{2}$
3.45 down	5	$32\frac{1}{2}$	$43\frac{1}{4}$	10	$9.10\frac{1}{4}$
4.15 up	9	$56\frac{1}{2}$	$32\frac{1}{4}$	15	$17.20\frac{1}{4}$
4.45 down	9	60	31	18	19.15
6.15 up	8	$38\frac{1}{4}$	$38\frac{1}{4}$	15	18.16
				277	$277.56\frac{1}{4}$

On 24 August the last meeting of the old London & Croydon company was held. The shareholders were told that the working expenses had been unduly high since atmospheric working began because of the locomotive help required, but, cautiously, that 'the atmospheric system . . . is satisfactorily progressing, and there is every reason to believe that it will fully realise . . . expectations . . . of ultimate success'. The half-yearly accounts showed £1,843 for 'stationary engines, for stores, wages, etc. and enginemen, firemen, superintendents, valvemen, groovemen, electric telegraphists, etc.'. For the following half year the figure was to fall to £1,547. The amalgamated company, now called the London, Brighton & South Coast, took over on 3 August, and with it the situation of atmospheric traction radically changed. Wilkinson, as vice-chairman of the new concern, unfortunately took the first shareholders' meeting, and rather tactlessly gave much of his speech to a restless audience to praise of the atmospheric, and his hopes of running 60 trains a day on the Croydon line.

Rastrick was the Brighton's engineer, but Cubitt was still concerned with the atmospheric line and the Epsom extension. He was interested in it as an engineering experiment, and wanted it to succeed; but he knew that traffic was outgrowing the power available. The tubes were too small, the engines too low-powered, properly to cope with the existing traffic, let alone that which would follow the opening of the Epsom extension. What to do? His solution was experimental: on 18 August he wrote: 'I consider the atmospheric system, as now at work and in progress towards completion, too important a matter either to be hastily extended or hastily thrown aside. My views are to complete the system in its present scale of pipes, &c., and as a single line from London to Croydon . . . to work it in the best manner, and to the full extent of its capabilities, through all seasons, and long enough to find out all its probable advantages and disadvantages; to ascertain precisely the cost of working it, and from experience, what modification would probably enlarge its use and reduce its costs, whether, by doubling the Line with the same sized pipe, or by working it as a single line with a larger pipe . . . till such time as this can be ascertained, my views further are, to open and work the Epsom line as a Locomotive line.'

The board's views were different. On the little London & Croydon it had been intended that all the commuter traffic would be worked atmospherically, separately from the use made of the Croydon metals by the long-distance trains of other companies. This would still have been so if Wilkinson's extensions had been built—to Epsom, to Portsmouth, into Kent—for they would all have connected with the atmospheric line, then perhaps doubled. Therefore locomotives would not normally have been needed at all. But the LBSCR had a large stock of locomotives and the staff to work and maintain them. To use them also for commuter traffic was likely to be far more economical than to maintain a separate traction system. Therefore, even if the atmospheric had been far more reliable than it was, the board's Brighton majority would not have been in favour of extending it, and would have sought to get rid of it as soon as possible.

They showed this by at once calling for a weekly report of atmospheric working expenses and suggestions for possible savings. The superintendent, Peter Clarke, who was hostile, on the basis of the figures for the one week ending 11 August, put in a statement of costs which showed a weekly wages bill for engine-house staff, fitters, and switchmen of £102 p.w. and that the three sets of engines were using 10 tons of coal a day at 14s a ton. This gave an operating cost in steam power alone of 12·2d per train mile.

Samuda put in a counter statement, on the one hand claiming that existing operating costs for power and maintenance of track on the atmospheric line were 19·7d per train mile, against 23d for the Croydon's locomotive lines and 23·25d for those of the former Brighton company, on the other that, whereas the existing engines could be improved, they could never be as economical as those he had designed for New Cross, London Bridge, and the Epsom line. Finally, he hinted that his efforts to make the line more efficient were not being helped by some of the new company's officers.

For some time after reopening, the Croydon line had worked well, the first delay occurring on 7 September, when the 4.15 from Croydon was 11 minutes late at Forest Hill, having had to be divided at the viaduct; the reason for lack of vacuum being given as shortage of water to the engines. A few days later the French Minister of Public Works, M. du Monde, and our old friend M. Teisserenc, Commissioner General of Railways, visited the Croydon before the first experimental trips were run on the Saint Germain line.

After this, working seems to have deteriorated, for this curious reason of lack of sufficient water supply. Businessmen complained loudly. There was delay anyway to change traction at Forest Hill and wait for the train coming the other way, and when a failure occurred a locomotive was only called in as a last resort, causing worse delay. The *Railway Chronicle*, not noticeably hostile, made inquiries, and wrote on 10 October: 'We have begun by inquiring of those City people who travel daily, and among them there is one undivided opinion against the atmospheric railway . . . irregularity, slowness, continual uncertainty and disappointment.' For the line's first six months, the engines had been blamed; then the valve and composition; now water supplies. There seemed no end to it. The paper then made its own investigations, and reached a more favourable conclusion. Trains up to eight or nine carriages could be worked at good speeds, and 60 mph was practicable for four loaded coaches: 'speed is money; 60 miles an hour is something worth paying for'. Expenses for maintaining the valve were falling, but 'as to cost and regularity, it cannot as yet be said to have proved anything'.

From early October, when presumably it rained enough to refresh the engines, running was good. 'Let this satisfactory condition be maintained for a few months and through the press of summer work,' said the *Chronicle* on 14 November, 'and it may then be time to look into the finance of the business—with some prospect of benefit from the examination.'

At the end of November 'the atmospheric engine-house at New

Cross is nearly completed, and a very ornamental building it is; far more in character for its purpose than the semi-ecclesiastical structures at Forest Hill and Croydon. It is built of party-coloured bricks—deep red and yellow; a spiral line of dark bricks ornamentally winds round the pale brick shaft of the chimney. The engine-house has rather an Italian character.'

In *The Times* for 18 December, Henry Hensman, replying to a complaint, claimed that out of 3,000 trains run during the preceding three months, only eleven had been delayed a quarter of an hour or more. Such statements must always be qualified by remembering that there were times when locomotive working was substituted, such as two half-days in early December when frost caused trouble; substitutions do not get quoted, only occasions when an atmospheric train had to be rescued by a locomotive.

On the Epsom extension the contractor was well behind, but was reaching the point of no return if a change in the traction system was to be made. Though Samuda now proposed to work the Epsom with only three additional engine-houses, and maintained that with better engines he could reduce operating costs, his were clearly not the views of most of the chief officers or of the board. In December 1846 the latter finally decided, as Cubitt had earlier agreed, that the Epsom line should be locomotive worked, and early in December asked Boulton & Watt what progress had been made on the engines that had been ordered for the extension, with a view to suspension or cancellation. The resignation of H. de Castro, a trustee of the atmospheric patent owners, from the LBSCR board on 2 December, was probably a result.

This decision at once added to the jeopardy of the Croydon line as a working entity and not an engineering experiment, for once the Epsom extension was opened, trains from Epsom would have to be changed from locomotives to piston carriages at Croydon, and back to locomotives at Forest Hill. In addition, insufficiency of power remained. The board's first idea was not to spend any more money on the atmospheric line, and in December they told

Samuda not to proceed with strengthening the engines at Croydon and Norwood to get more power. In the past also the railway company had paid the salary of Hensman, Samuda's manager and the cost of alterations to the apparatus. Now the same December board asked Samuda whether he would be willing to contract to work the Croydon traffic for a term of years; to hurry him up they refused any longer to pay Hensman's salary. By February 1847 Samuda had put in a draft agreement to work the line for fixed monthly payments for four years, terminable by either side on payment of a fine. This encouraged the LBSC sufficiently to authorise Samuda to see Maudslay's about strengthening the two sets of engines, though at the same time telling him to see if he could dispose of those engines and tubes Boulton & Watt were making. He could not, and Boulton & Watt were paid to stop work and keep them.

On 14 January tests were held on the New Cross incline. The first train of four coaches (including the piston carriage) weighing 16 to 17 tons, carried the Government inspector, Captain Coddington, Wilkinson, Samuda, and others non-stop from New Cross to Croydon, $7\frac{1}{2}$ miles, at 36 mph. Seven coaches (31–32 tons) came back, and were then taken from New Cross to Forest Hill at an average of 20 mph start to stop. At Forest Hill the tube ended at one side of the station, and began again at the other. As it was downhill both ways from the platform, presumably stopping trains started again by gravity.

With the Samuda agreement in force, though details had not been agreed, the board on 19 February met shareholders as hostile to the atmospheric system as they. The chairman set the tone: 'looking at the uncertainty of the atmospheric mode, they were always compelled to have locomotives to take up the traffic which the atmospheric left on their hands' (hear, hear). . . . But it would not have been right for them to force upon their new allies a different system from that which their allies had chosen, and so the agreement with Samuda had been made. Now, 'if locomotives should be brought into play—that was to be at his expense—not ours (loud applause). Nothing would induce him to consent to the continuance of the system one moment longer than it ought to be carried on' (continued applause). This was too much for Wilkinson, now vice-chairman, who leapt to the defence of the system. 'Everything had been done in it, not only with the sanction, but under the advice of one of the first engineers of the country, Mr Cubitt . . . the question of the practicability of the atmospheric system had been quite established (no, no). . . . The point for them to look at was certainly the economy, and he saw that they had now let the line at a less rate per train per mile than they ever had yet.' (Noise and interruption).

Three days later the board agreed to the immediate extension of atmospheric working for another $2\frac{1}{2}$ miles from Forest Hill to New Cross, much of it at 1 in 100, and the bringing into use of the engine-house there when ready. Public working began about 27 February, using the second pair of engines at Forest Hill for upwards working (those at New Cross never got to work before the line closed), and gravity downwards. Maybe they acted genuinely, though Samuda had asked for certain work to be done first. But as the sequel so conveniently disposed both of Samuda and Cubitt, and as the shareholders' views were so clear, it is likely that they did not.

The New Cross incline proved too much for unaided atmospheric traction. Locomotives could pull well-filled trains from London Bridge to New Cross, but the 15 in tube and low-powered stationary engines were inadequate to get them up the bank without help, as the board knew perfectly well. As Cubitt was soon to say : 'the increase of traffic has been much more than was probably contemplated when the scale of the atmospheric apparatus was determined on, and from this cause . . . the size of the tube (15 in), tho' sufficient for the level portions of the line, is unsuited to the severe gradient of the New Cross incline, to deal with trains of sufficient magnitude to work in conjunction with the locomotive arrangements'.

Delays increased, though they were probably not so bad as the company later alleged, or as few as the system's apologists claimed : a few were caused by severe frosts, some by underpowering, some by an undeclared state of war between Samuda and LBSC officials. For instance, a paragraph in the 24 April issue of the *Railway Record* says: 'During the last few weeks, four trains have got off the line, and considerable damage has been done to the piston carriage, solely, from the circumstance that the new switchmen, put in by Mr Peter Clarke, to supersede the experienced men, have not known their duty.' One guesses the information to have come from Samuda. One temporary solution, to extend the atmospheric line to London Bridge so that lighter and more frequent trains could be worked up to the line's full capacity, was ruled out because the SER had not yet started their widening, though a bill had been introduced to enable the LBSC to do it instead. Again, the Epsom extension was almost ready, and offered all the difficulties not only of a second traction change at Croydon for through trains from London Bridge, but of heavy trains to be worked right through when the race traffic began on 15 May. And so, in April, the Locomotive & Construction Committee minuted:

'The Committee having had under their consideration the returns of delays on the atmospheric line, wherefrom it appeared that great irregularities exist, and being cognizant of the very great dissatisfaction for a long time past evinced by the Passengers thereby, having deemed it necessary to confer with Mr Cubitt on the subject, and finding it to be his opinion that the atmospheric apparatus as it now exists is not adequate to the requirements of the Croydon traffic, and that he cannot advise the Company to incur an additional outlay for the purpose of making it so', recommended that in future the line should be worked by locomotives. Cubitt clearly saw no alternative but to agree, though he said squarely: 'this does not arise in my mind from any conviction that the atmospheric system cannot be made to work, which its previous and present action on this line sufficiently disproves'.

On 3 May the board accepted the committee's report, and ordered Samuda, who was in Devon at the time, to be told that locomotive working would start the following day. He naturally reacted violently to an action which seems unnecessarily brutal: 'the atmospheric power was suitably prepared and ready to take the trains as usual until the company by violent means broke up, and removed the pipes along a portion of the line, the vacuum being then in the pipes, and thus intercepting and preventing the working of the trains under his contract'. He complained that necessary works had not been carried out, and demanded ample compensation. Two directors were told off to meet him. A week later, on 10 May, the Epsom extension opened.

The *Railway Chronicle*'s surprise supports the probability that the decision to close preceded thought about the reasons: 'We confess our surprise at this sudden resolve. . . . Never before was the atmospheric doing so well, going so regularly, working so economically. The directors hàve for a couple of months been working a contract with Mr Samuda, which . . . gives them atmospheric power at less cost than the locomotive, and Mr Samuda is said to have been well pleased with his contract, and the public service well performed . . . this sudden resolution of the Board . . . will . . . deprive all parties of the advantage of an unbiased decision'.

The comment from *Herapath's Railway Journal* was rather different: 'We have been asked, What will be done with the four engine-houses, *alias* churches on the Croydon line? It has been suggested that Mr Wilkinson takes one to live in; Mr Samuda another; and that the two others be made a church and a synagogue for them to pray daily in, for the sin of wasting so much of innocent Shareholders' money.'

Within a few weeks orders were given to dismantle the wooden viaduct, let the engine-houses, sell the engines and tubes, including Boulton & Watt's, and withdraw the bill enforcing the additional line to London Bridge. A letter from the Railway Commissioners at the end of May saying that they must inspect the line before locomotives could use it arrived rather too late, though in August the shareholders were told that 'From an insufficiency of power, by atmospheric traction, to work the Epsom, in addition to the Croydon traffic, your Directors by the advice of their Consulting Engineer, and with the sanction of the Railway Commissioners, have substituted Locomotive power.'

It took some years to clear up Samuda's claims and those of the patent holders, proceedings that were enlivened by the beginning of a legal action by Pinkus against the company for allowing Samuda to invade his rights, which got no further than Pinkus's other efforts. Slowly the engines were sold. The valve leather was offered in Northampton, and realised £8 per ton, presumably finishing up as boots. The tubes were disposed of in various lots, but some were used to underpin a slipping embankment on the down side at Haywards Heath, where presumably they still are. During rebuilding at West Croydon in 1933, when the last traces of the 1839 station disappeared, some old tubes were unearthed. Croydon engine-house was taken down and re-erected near Surrey Street for use as a waterworks pumping station, whilst Forest Hill, latterly a milk depot, stood until it was destroyed by a flying bomb in 1944.

The principal cause of the Croydon's closure was lack of power : a tube too small, and engines inadequate, for the increasing weight of commuter trains. This underpowering was made worse by the single track, for the remedy of running lighter trains more frequently could only be used up to its capacity, while delays were cumulative. Therefore we see the engines being worked at high vacuum, practicable only when they and the valve were in really good condition. Here we have a major disadvantage of the atmospheric system, the high capital cost of increasing the power available, by laying down a larger tube and installing bigger engines, or of doubling the track as an alternative.

The secondary cause was the failure of Samuda's improved valve, for it caused a six weeks' shut-down that had fatal effects. It decided the London & Croydon directors that atmospheric traction would not be safe on the Epsom extension, prejudiced the London & Brighton board at a critical moment, probably encouraged the South Eastern to delay widening the track to London Bridge, and caused the public to lose confidence in the system. They never regained it. These decisions in turn made it certain that the cost and inconvenience of switching the mode of traction at New Cross and again at Croydon would lead to closure of the atmospheric line as soon as the Epsom extension was ready.

Yet the supporters of the atmospheric saw and understood surprisingly early the need for fast, frequent commuter services, and provided them. To operate 39 suburban trains, heavy for their time, reasonably fast over a single track each week-day and almost as many on Sunday, was an achievement in its day. Among those present at a meeting in December 1847 of passengers on the Croydon and Epsom line to complain of high fares, unpunctuality and bad accommodation, were there any who looked back to wonder whether more could not have been made of the tube and its stationary engines, or dared to regret the old days of cleanliness and quiet?

CHAPTER NINE

THE SOUTH DEVON IS PLANNED

O N 1 May 1844 the Bristol and Exeter Railway was completed to Exeter, at a time when a bill was in Parliament for a line onwards to Plymouth; it was passed on 4 July, authorising a capital of £1,100,000, of which £400,000 would be subscribed by the Great Western, Bristol & Exeter, and Bristol & Gloucester companies, and the South Devon* began its stormy career, guided by a board of twenty-one, eleven of whom were nominated by the associated companies. The plans had been made, and the bill passed, on the assumption of a double-track locomotive line.

Brunel had made some experiments at Wormwood Scrubs in 1840: 'I found that the atmospheric pipe and the valve laid down . . . did . . . produce very fair results as to the power of traction; that a moderate exhaustion of the pipe was easily attained . . . the working of the valve appeared to me to be sufficiently satisfactory to lead me, at that time, to expect that the system might be worked out after further improvements in the construction; but I took no further interest in the matter then', though he did consider whether it was applicable to the Box tunnel incline.

When the Dalkey line began to work, he made two or three visits. They strengthened his conviction, and in January 1844 his name appeared as engineer of the Gravesend, Rochester & Chatham atmospheric railway. In May 1844, after the bill for that line had been thrown out, and about a month after the Dalkey opened to public use, Brunel supported the atmospheric

* This account only deals with atmospheric traction on the South Devon. For a history of the line generally, see E. T. Macdermot (revised by C. R. Clinker), *History of the Great Western Railway*, II, 103 ff.

system against Robert Stephenson before the Parliamentary Committee on the Croydon and Epsom. There he was asked whether he intended to introduce it on the South Devon, and replied: 'I have not been called upon to recommend it or not.'

Indeed, the board met for the first time on 5 July. A month later they received a letter from Samuda Bros suggesting that the system be used because of its advantages in cheap construction and haulage, and in surmounting steep gradients. One presumes that Brunel had instigated the letter, for by 19 August he had reported, and in the meantime Thomas Gill, the chairman, and other notabilities of the company had visited Dalkey. They were much impressed, especially by the operating costs Bergin gave them.

Brunel's report was short, and began with some sweeping statements. 'I shall assume . . . that stationary power, if free from the weight and friction of any medium of communication, as a rope, must be cheaper, is more under command, and is susceptible of producing much higher speeds than Locomotive power', with its great weight in relation to total weight hauled. 'I . . . assume also that, as a means of applying Stationary power, the atmospheric system . . . is a good and economical mode.' True, Robert Stephenson disagrees and has published detailed data, but such calculations depend upon 'an unattained precision in experiments', and 'experience has led me to prefer . . . a *practical* view'. Working at Dalkey showed that the system 'may be considered practically to be free from any mechanical objection'; the loss of vacuum by leakage or friction was small enough not to be taken into consideration, and what is true of one length of line is not altered by multiplying the lengths. Four inclines on the South Devon, making up one-fifth of the whole, would in any case have to be worked by stationary power. By having a single atmospheric line instead of double tracks for locomotives, increasing gradients, reducing the radius of curves, and building single-line structures, £207,000 could be saved, plus another £50,000 for locomotives and their sheds. Against this the new system could be installed for £190,000, plus £160 a mile for the

XVII. *Dawlish in single-track broad-gauge days. The engine-house and the station with its overall roof date from the atmospheric line*

xviii. *South Devon engine-houses at (above) Newton and (below) Totnes*

electric telegraph. Before the Select Committee, Brunel estimated the cost of the tube as £3,300 a mile and the engine-houses with their engines at £5,100 each. He ended by listing the real advantages of atmospheric traction as high speeds—40 to 50 mph up the gradients and round the curves, against 30 mph with a locomotive, the possibility of running frequent trains cheaply, less noise, motion and dust for travellers, and £8,000 p.a. saved in the cost of working. And so : 'I have no hesitation in taking upon myself the full and certain responsibility of recommending the adoption of the Atmospheric System on the South Devon Railway, and of recommending as a consequence that the line and works should be constructed for a single Line only.'

The board agreed at once, and so did the shareholders, meeting at Plymouth on 28 August. So a broad-gauge line, mainly single-track, but with certain double-track sections, as on the inclines, was decided upon, 52 miles long from Exeter by way of Newton Abbot and Totnes to Plymouth. The autumn was spent in negotiation with the Samudas on patent rights and the supply of the valve and fittings, with Cooke & Wheatstone for the telegraph, to be installed on the railway's whole length, and with ordering engines from Boulton & Watt, G. & J. Rennie, and Maudslay, Son & Field. There were discussions also on branches and connecting lines to Tavistock and Launceston, Torquay, and possibly Dartmouth. Later Exmouth was to be added.

More important, agreement was reached with the provisional committee of the Cornwall Railway, of which Brunel was also engineer, that it would adopt the broad gauge and atmospheric traction. It brought a letter from Charles Russell of the Great Western, one of the associated companies, to say that his company had assumed a double-track line on the South Devon as the basis of their assistance unless it should prove unduly expensive. As for the atmospheric, the Great Western nominees were 'unfavourable to the experiment being made for so long a line without a further opportunity of testing it'. They had not felt justified in opposing the decision of the rest of the South

K

Devon board, but remained apprehensive, and the Great Western could 'by no means be considered as a party entertaining an opinion favourable to the adoption of the atmospheric principle with the present amount of experience'. It brought the Cornwall directors another, this time from Charles Saunders, which suggested firmly that they should choose locomotives. They did not

Extent of line comprehended in the license

1st Exeter to Plymouth

2nd Branches at Plymouth to Sutton Pool, Mill bay and New Passage

3o Branch to Tavistock
And any sidings or branches consequent on these and within the ordinary powers of the said acts of Parliament.

March 22nd 1845

Part of the agreement signed by Brunel and Samuda for installing atmospheric apparatus

feel they could go back on their agreement, but replied that they would only adopt the atmospheric if it were found preferable. With this the Great Western had to be content; after all it was their own engineer who was so strongly advocating it.

A shareholders' meeting in February 1845 had been told that it was hoped to open the section from Exeter to Newton* in July. The chairman said: 'there was but little doubt but that there would be an Atmospheric Line of Railway from Exeter to

---

* Not called Newton Abbot until 1877.

the Land's End; great advantages would result in lessened costs of working of the continuous atmospheric line, as compared with what it would cost if different systems of locomotion were employed. As to the atmospheric system itself, it was now being adopted in almost every part of the country, and, notwithstanding the *Northern Leviathan** had said it was "A Humbug", the Directors of the South Devon were satisfied.'

In March Brunel signed an agreement with Samuda on behalf of the trustees (the others were H. de Castro and F. I. Van Zeller) of Clegg's patent of 3 January 1839 and the Samudas' subsequent patent of 30 April 1844 for improvements. It provided that the South Devon would pay £250 per mile on its opening for public service, and another £250 per mile a year later, up to a total of £25,000. A month earlier he had signed the contract for the valve, which provided that Samuda would keep it in repair for twelve months 'after each portion shall have been in work for the public traffic'.

At another meeting in June a shareholder asked whether the South Devon directors were as decidedly in favour of the atmospheric system as before. The chairman replied that the 'confidence of the Directors in the atmospheric system . . . had actually risen higher since the holding of the former meeting, and this effect he believed had been produced to a still greater extent upon the mind of their Engineer'. He added that doubts were not surprising, considering the attacks that had been made on the system, and the examination before the Select Committee.

During the summer there was a continued interest in branch lines, support for the proposed North Devon Railway from Crediton to Barnstaple, a possible atmospheric line, and a letter from Pinkus's solicitor warning the company that he was the true inventor and patentee of the system they proposed to use. In August Brunel, reporting progress, said that 'some delay had arisen from his having wished to watch the operations of the Croydon line, which was so shortly to be opened'. Testing began there in the same month.

* George Stephenson.

It had originally been intended to provide the South Devon with three different sizes of tube, each powered by a pair of engines of appropriate horse-power, an expanding piston being used when passing from a smaller to a large diameter: 13 in (80 hp the pair), 15 in (100 hp) and 22 in (160/170 hp). The original contract for the tubes for the Exeter–Newton section had been for 4,400 tons of 13 in diameter, placed with George Hennet. Hennet, whose address was 16 Duke Street, Westminster (Brunel's was No 18), was a contractor who seems to have had his own foundry, but who also undertook permanent way construction, the building of stations and engine-houses and similar work on the South Devon. Seemingly the company in atmospheric days never had a written contract with him, and work proceeded on the basis of uncompetitive tenders. While the tubes were being made under difficulties in obtaining the iron, Brunel, presumably as a result of Croydon experience, altered the diameter to 15 in, and placed a new order with Tayleur & Sanderson of Warrington as well as with Hennet, about 1,500 13 in tubes already made being laid aside. But the 80 hp pairs of engines had already been ordered, and at design stage they were therefore provided with auxiliary engines to increase their net power output. A better alternative would have been larger pumps.

Under P. G. Margery's control, the work of building engine-houses began at the end of April 1845. He took charge of construction, but each manufacturer had his own foreman to get his engines erected. Some heavy parts of these, such as the boilers, came by sea to be landed at Topsham or Teignmouth, the rest by rail. The engine-houses planned between Exeter and Newton, with their approximate distances in miles from Exeter and the engine suppliers, were: Exeter (Boulton & Watt), Countess Wear, 3 miles (Rennie), Turf, 5½ miles (Boulton & Watt), Starcross, 8½ miles (Boulton & Watt), Dawlish, 12 miles (Maudslay's), Teignmouth, 15 miles (Rennie), Summerhouse, 18 miles (Maudslay's), and Newton, 20 miles (Rennie). Each contained two large 40 hp and two small 12 hp engines, and were provided with reservoirs or other means of supplying water, and with sidings for coal trucks.

Tube-laying began before Christmas 1845, by which time some track had been laid and was being used by steam-hauled construction trains. Brunel told the restless shareholders again, at the end of February 1846, that 'in my desire to profit by the experience of the Croydon Railway, I have intentionally, and I think wisely, postponed mere matters of detail, which has caused considerable delay in the completion of this part of the machinery necessary for our opening. The success of this system upon the Croydon Railway has fully confirmed me in the views I entertained of its applicability to this Railway'.

A Board meeting on 14 April had asked Brunel what arrangements he had made for tubes and stationary engines beyond Newton. In fact, he had made none. It was not until July that he approved 22 in tube for working this section, or August that the board accepted Boulton & Watt's tender for six pairs of bigger engines, 136 hp the pair, at £6,600 per pair, for this part of the line. Nothing was done about the engine-houses until April 1847.

To encourage the board when it met again on 16 May, Samuda told them that the Croydon line was working satisfactorily, unfortunately just before it shut down for six weeks to renew the valve. Meanwhile few engines had yet been installed between Exeter and Newton. A complaint of late delivery of theirs for Dawlish and Summerhouse was sent to Maudslay's, and on 8 June Brunel wrote to Carr, the South Devon's secretary: 'I am urging Boulton & Watts, Rennies, &c. all I possibly can with the engines . . . but all the world has more to do than they can get through.' On Saturday 30 May 1846 the South Devon line was opened between Exeter and Teignmouth for passengers only with steam locomotives hired from the Great Western at 1s 4d a train mile. At first the trains took 45 minutes, later 40.

To others, Brunel used the six weeks stoppage on the Croydon to advantage, telling the Parliamentary committee on the Exeter

& Yeovil Railway that 'I have, perhaps cowardly or prudently, delayed the final working of the South Devon line . . . till the Croydon Company have had the kindness to pay for these experiments.' But to the South Devon board he became especially elusive. On 7 July they minuted: 'The Directors repeat their desire that Mr Brunel will either in person or by Deputy make a point of attending their Meetings, and that he will report regularly the state and progress of the Works, and lay before the Board all future Tenders for Contracts, and afford full particulars of all Contracts now existing.' They knew, of course, about the valve trouble on the Croydon, and were much disturbed. A fortnight later a sub-committee was appointed to talk to Brunel about the state of progress and of contracts for engines and tubes, and with him and Samuda on the 'present state of the atmospheric apparatus on the Croydon Railway'; he must have reassured them, or they would not have agreed to order the Boulton & Watt engines.

A shareholders' meeting on 5 September heard that 10,000 passengers a week were being carried to and from Teignmouth, and that £154,784 had so far been spent on atmospheric equipment. Brunel's report told them that the locomotive working 'holds out a fair promise of the line running remarkably smoothly and perfectly, when the absence of the locomotive engine shall admit of more perfect and easy maintenance of correctness in the rails'. The tube was laid nearly to Newton, the valve was about to be fixed, but the engines were not ready, and could not be for some weeks, though those at Exeter had been tried. On the other hand, the Croydon stoppage had improved the composition to be used. 'In a few weeks,' he said, 'we shall at least be enabled to run trains, though perhaps not entirely dispensing with the locomotives; and I feel convinced that the result will repay you for the anxiety of waiting.' By now the Cornwall Railway had been authorised, as had a Torquay branch in 1845 as far as Torre. But that to Tavistock, and the Exeter, Topsham & Exmouth, both of which would have been atmospheric, had failed. On 30 December the main line was extended to Newton, still with locomotives and for passengers. Goods working began on 1 May 1847.

At the end of November Samuda agreed to rent a company house at Dawlish for a year as a base for his work on the line, and at last, on 2 January 1847, the Exeter engines were properly run. The telegraph was pressed forward, and hurry increased as Brunel made it known that he wanted his first test. Turf engines started on 4 February, Dawlish on the 16th; on the 17th the tube was ready to Turf, and on the 23rd the engines at Countess Wear and Starcross were started—Countess Wear not for long, as the eccentrics broke.

Then on 25 February the first piston carriage came down to Exeter from the carriage works on the 3.15 train, and at 6 p.m. was sent to Turf behind a locomotive to clear the water and dirt out of the tube. A few days later the first test train, the piston carriage and another, was run from Exeter to Turf, using only one engine-house to exhaust the whole tube: the Turf engines when going to Turf, and Exeter engines on the return trip. Thereafter test trains were run to Turf on most days, extending to Starcross on 18 March. On 22 March the tube was cleared to Dawlish, and so work went on, much held up by delays in finishing the engine-houses and various troubles with the engines.

In February 1847, with land purchasing powers running out, the board had asked Brunel immediately to fix sites for engine-houses and stations below Newton, to contract for the engine-houses, and to tell the board when he had done so. Hopefully they sought from their engineer a fortnightly plan of work done below Newton. In April they asked him when the atmospheric could open to Teignmouth, added that 'in the present imperfect state of atmospheric arrangements' he should consult the board before making further payments to Samuda, and ended by complaining of the slow progress of the South Devon compared to other lines; would he please appoint a full-time engineer under himself who would attend board meetings?

This was the first symptom of real unease about the future of their system. It was followed in early May by the news that the Croydon line had shut down, before any part of theirs was publicly open. They were naturally most alarmed. When they met on the 11th, Brunel was not there, and in reply to directors' worried inquiries 'how far the reported abandonment of the atmospheric system on the Croydon Line was occasioned by circumstances which should be allowed to influence the South Devon Board', Gill said that their engineer had given explanations 'of a satisfactory nature'. Samuda, embarrassed though he must have felt, attended the board to say that the tube and engines were complete to Dawlish, and that test trains had been run satisfactorily. The engines at Teignmouth were almost ready, and the board could rely upon 'having the whole of the atmospheric completed and ready for traffic on the 15th of next month'. It seems, however, that the board made up its mind on the spot not to extend atmospheric working beyond Totnes for the time being. Nevertheless, Brunel not only set Margery to finish the plans for Dainton engine-house, next after Newton, but chose a site for Torre on the Torquay branch, and for Totnes, Rattery, Wrangaton and Ivybridge on the main line.

At a shareholders' meeting late in May, worried by sinister reports of the atmospheric, the chairman explained the Croydon shut-down as 'a matter of expediency. It was inexpedient to have two systems of traction within so short a distance of each other, and because one was often an obstacle to the other; and that eminent engineer, Mr Cubitt, was only induced to assent to it on that account. The public are not quite aware of that.' He went on to say that their own line had been repeatedly worked between Exeter and Dawlish in every possible way, both by heavy weights and light weights, and all the experiments had been eminently successful with respect to both. Speeds of 70 mph with light weights, and of 30–35 mph with loads of 90 to 100 tons had been obtained, 'so that we have no doubts in our own minds of the success of the atmospheric (cheers). We do not wish to open it for a less distance than 15   s. It can be but a very short time before we shall use the atmospheric, and the atmospheric only, as far as Teignmouth (cheers). We are making the utmost effort to complete the engines between Teignmouth and Newton, and in three months we hope to get those engines ready.' He added that the line to Totnes should be open for locomotive traction in a fortnight, and that to Plymouth would soon follow.

Early in June there was a disastrous test in the presence of some of the directors: owing to valve trouble the speed varied between 60 and 12 mph, and once the train stopped dead. But on 26 June Samuda wrote to the board that trains had been run to Teignmouth and: 'I think I may rely on having sufficient Piston Carriages on the line and the starting arrangements at the Stations finished and ready for traffic in a fortnight from this.' But the Dawlish engines 'do not yet work satisfactorily, and tho' I have relied on Messrs Maudslay to have rectified whatever is amiss with them, I had hoped and fully expected Mr Field would have come down and taken the matter personally in hand'; but he had not, though Brunel also had pressed him.

On 20 July the Railway Commissioners authorised the opening of the South Devon to Totnes for locomotives, but asked why the gradients had been altered. Brunel replied that those each side of Dainton tunnel had been changed from 1 in 52 in the Parliamentary plans to 1 in 42/43 because of difficulties with the rock formations. This had not troubled him 'considering that these two inclines as well as the two others on the line would eventually be worked by stationary assistant power'.

On 3 August Brunel reported that amospheric working to Teignmouth could start in a few days, and suggested that this should be done 'by the addition of a few atmospheric short trains'. This was agreed, and they started to run on Monday 16 August, when Samuda reported that all 'were run punctually and had time on the journey to spare'. He added that the Dawlish engines had had new steam pipes and condensers, and were decidedly improved. The same were due for Summerhouse, which also had Maudslay engines, and 'ought to have been here long before'.

Brunel's report of 27 August attributes the long three years' delay since, in August 1844, he had so confidently recommended atmospheric traction, 'principally, if not entirely, in that part of the whole system which it might have been expected would have been the least exposed to it—namely, the construction and completion of the Steam Engines . . . the engines, though designed without any interference with their plans and furnished by the first makers of the country, and although differing so slightly from the ordinary construction of steam engines, have proved sources of continued and most vexatious delays both in the unexpected length of time occupied originally in their erection and in subsequent correction of defects in minor parts . . . the frequent interruptions to the continuous working of all the Engines rendered it impossible to test and complete the different portions of the Atmospheric Apparatus. . . . Since the beginning of last week, however, four trains per day have been run regularly, stopping at the Stations and keeping their time as if working for traffic . . . running in this manner can alone show the deficiencies which may still exist in the details necessary for stopping and starting quickly from the stations and all the minor operations.' He went on to say that the two engines nearest Newton were nearly ready for trial. Difficulties had been aggravated by the working of the line by locomotives while the atmospheric apparatus was being installed; one consequence being that 'it has been necessary to devise all the arrangements so as to admit Stations, Sidings and Line being worked either by Locomotive or by Atmospheric in succession, or even at the same time.' Meanwhile the Torquay branch was nearly ready.

There are more sides than one to most stories. Another to Brunel's complaints about the engines is given in a letter of 28 May 1847 to him from G. & J. Rennie. 'In reply to that part of your letter of yesterday's date complaining that you are waiting for our Engines, we beg to say that these Engines were ready for delivery agreeably to our Contract nearly two years since, and that subsequently we have met with such repeated interruptions for want of the Engine Houses, and other preparations being ready to receive them, that it has been impossible to pro-

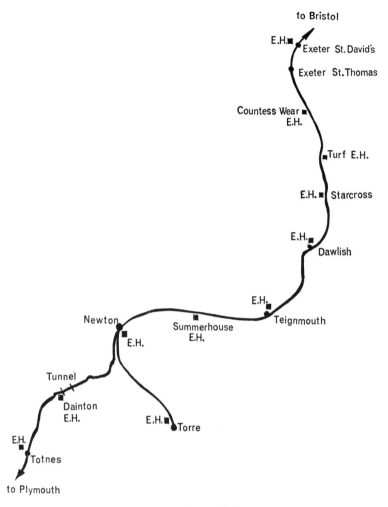

The South Devon Railway

ceed with the erection of them faster . . . even now the Engines at the Teignmouth Station are ready to start, but there are no coals to work them, as you will see from the enclosed letter from our Assistant, Mr Humphreys.'

On the day after Brunel's report, that before the half-yearly shareholders' meeting, the board considered a letter from George Hudson and the Midland Railway directors who now sat on the South Devon board to represent the old Bristol & Gloucester interest. They asked that no expense for atmospheric working beyond Totnes should be incurred until the following share-holders' meeting, and in the meantime locomotives should be taken off as soon as possible so that the utility of the atmospheric system might be fully tried between Exeter and Totnes. The board replied that they did not intend to incur any more expenses beyond Totnes 'until the system between Exeter and Totnes shall have been fairly tried, except to provide Assistant Power up the two inclines, which will be necessary under any circum-stances'. This new compromise seems here to be mentioned for the first time—the inclines meant were Rattery and Hemerdon near Plymouth. After this the timber viaducts on the Plymouth line were strengthened to take locomotives.

On 29 August the shareholders met at Plymouth. Gill, the chairman, was firm that an experiment that ended at Newton would be no experiment at all : if the atmospheric was successful on the gradients to Totnes, it should convince everyone. While this section was proving itself, the engines beyond Totnes would be helping trains on the banks until atmospheric working was extended over the whole line. Hudson, 'regretted for himself and . . . for the company he represented, that the South Devon line was involved in an expensive system, but . . . as they had pro-ceeded so far, it was due to the public, it was due to the inventor . . . that it should be fairly and properly tried' (loud cheers). He added that even if its tractive power proved superior, maybe its cost would prove too high for the locality through which it ran.

The *Western Times* disliked Hudson. After referring to 'King Hudson, whose tractive power in raising the wind, like Mr Samuda's, had by the late "depression" been over-taxed', went on to refer to his spy on the Croydon 'who had been for some months occupied in travelling by every atmospheric train; he timed all the starting and stopping, he chronicled all the mishaps of the nascent invention . . . the slightest hitch anywhere brought him out . . . he was ever prying about among the workmen and assistants of all classes . . . he worked out to a bushel how much coal was consumed per day, and when he backed up his statements . . . with details tending to show that the cost of working it . . . was greater than the cost of the locomotive would be— he administered a death blow to the hopes of all but those who were most hopeful'. And so the Croydon had been closed. They added, trimming their sails to western winds, that Hudson's witness should have made the South Devon cautious of pressing on. However, it was hopeful that Brunel was blaming the engines. If they were perfected, and Mr Samuda proved that 'he has got the valve', the future should look more economical.

On 10 September test trains fitted with a dynamometer were run : six coaches loaded to 62 tons reached 52 mph, and eight carrying 78 tons ran at 42 mph in a high wind. Samuda was satisfied, and on Monday 13 September the public service began.

It was on a theme of high cost that the South Devon opened its atmospheric line. It was on the same theme that, almost a year later, it closed.

CHAPTER TEN

THE SOUTH DEVON AT WORK

IN August 1847 James Pearson from the London & Croydon had been appointed Superintendent of the Atmospheric Department at £300 a year. On 7 September a ball was given at Sea Lawn House, Dawlish, by the engineers of the South Devon Railway. Brunel seems not to have been there, but Mrs Brunel came, and Mr and Mrs Samuda. It must have been a hopeful occasion, for on Monday 13 September 1847 two atmospheric trains a day began running in each direction between Exeter and Teignmouth in addition to the ordinary service of seven a day (three on Sundays) plus goods trains, then being hauled by locomotives between Exeter and Totnes. The new trains started well, the 4 p.m. on Tuesday being very crowded, but doing the journey in 22 minutes running time. Samuda from his Dawlish office, helped by Hensman, former atmospheric manager of the London & Croydon, watched the running, having ordered 'that any Atmospheric delay however trifling shall be at the earliest possible time sent to me'. But already the comment was being made that if the system stopped at Totnes, it was doomed, for different forms of traction were as bad as a break of gauge.

On Saturday evening the 25th, Brunel and Samuda did a non-stop test run from St Thomas's to Teignmouth in 17 minutes (the present express timing is about 21 minutes, not of course with such a light train): 'lightning itself looks not half so mysterious as did this string of carriages, flying, without any cause attached', wrote the local reporter. On the 27th three ordinary trains a day and a goods, were transferred to atmospheric working, the complete passenger service being increased in October

158

to eight, each way (four on Sundays). A locomotive was put on at Teignmouth to trains going beyond, which took the whole train, piston-carriage included, as far as Newton. On the return journey the piston-carriage was put on again at Newton behind the engine, which was detached at Teignmouth. Three men of the atmospheric department could now relax sufficiently to get married, all to Devon girls. By mid-October the service was running pretty well, though the board, annoyed by Hudson's criticisms at the shareholders' meeting, did not take kindly to the arrival of his observer Mr Winter, sent with a request that he might study the atmospheric working. They sent him home, minuting their 'disinclination . . . to admit Mr Winter to the Works'. After Winter's efforts on the Croydon, one is not surprised.

'Much heavier trains are brought than we were led to expect', reported a newspaper, though an occasional goods train failed and had to be moved by locomotive—and the 'novelty of the thing begins to disappear : passengers go in and out with the same indifference and confidence they would manifest towards a stage coach. Master Piston is getting a general favourite. Indeed many prefer his noiseless track to the long drawn sighs of "Puffing Billy", and often wait to bear the former young gentleman company.' By the end of the month the full train service was nine each day (four on Sundays), two of which only ran between Exeter and Teignmouth.

But valve decay had begun, and passengers saw sections of old valve lying beside the line, though the service seems to have been regular. It was, however, being maintained 'by the aid of a body of men along the line, who are constantly at work with short blunt sticks, rubbing the grease against the valve, to stop the leaks'. Another trouble was rainwater collecting on the valve channel, then leaking into the tube and settling at the bottom, so obstructing the piston. This happened especially at night, when no trains were running, and a pilot piston-carriage had then to be run in the early mornings to clear the tube.

Later the telegraph was used successfully between Newton and

Exeter to warn the police there that a woman thief had caught the train at Newton. Here we come to a major puzzle. There are plenty of indications in the local Press—such as this one— that the telegraph had been installed at stations, and worked well; indeed, the public does not seem to have thought otherwise. Yet Brunel told the board in mid-October that the telegraph was not working satisfactorily, and at the February 1848 shareholders' meeting his main complaint was that without it communications could not be maintained between the engine-houses, and therefore the engines were overdriven and used excessive fuel.

It seems likely that to begin with the telegraph was only installed at the stations, which could cover, though inconveniently, five out of the eight engine-houses, the exceptions being Countess Wear, Turf, and Summerhouse. Though Margery's diary for January 1847 records that he had been ordered to put it into engine-houses themselves, this work was not completed until 2 August 1848, and was probably not begun until early in that year. The accounts show £1,001 spent on the telegraph for the first six months of 1848, against £4,014 previously: this must have included a good deal of new installation. Again, the *Railway Chronicle* of 18 March 1848, referring to the crossing of trains at Starcross for the first time, says: 'The efficient working of the telegraph, which is now being arranged in the various engine-houses, will enable this arrangement of crossing trains to be carried out at any intermediate station.' Except in Brunel's reports, I have found no hint that the telegraph did not at any time work properly; it was in fact installed late, and has been unjustly blamed.

On Tuesday 16 November an experimental atmospheric train left Teignmouth at 9.55 a.m., stopped four minutes at Summerhouse engine-house, and reached Newton at 10.08; this month three more members of the engineering staff got engaged. A change was now made to winter composition for the valve; it was presumably that formerly used on the Croydon line. Trains on one day had been delayed half an hour at Countess Wear:

XIX. *(left) Old 22 inch atmospheric tubes used as a drain; (above) a section of similar tube; (below) a piston carriage and 'police constable' on the South Devon, from a contemporary painting*

xx. *The track, sidings and engine-house of the Saint Germain line, outside Saint Germain station*

frost was blamed, but it turned out that the enginemen had let their fires down. One of the air-pumps at Teignmouth broke, though the other was used during repairs without causing delays. In December the engine-house at Totnes was progressing well.

From the beginning of December till early February Devon had some very cold weather, and frost caused a number of serious delays to services, and a good deal of annoyance to passengers, which was made the most of by critics, such as *Woolmer's Exeter & Plymouth Gazette*. Even the *Western Times*, a steady supporter, was mildly critical when on 28 December the up mail train was delayed an hour at Dawlish with a frozen valve. The clerk of the station was absent, and further time was lost before telegraphing for a locomotive, which made the passengers crosser. Yet only on one day, 18 January, when a sudden frost occurred, was running really disorganised, with locomotives brought in to help on two others, during which the thermometer had been continually below freezing point. In February loco-motives were used on some trains on about six days. After that the cold weather ended.

Yet at the beginning of January the *Western Times'* Dawlish correspondent had written: 'our pleasant and healthy little watering-place continues to remain full', and added, 'I think we may with all our heart say success to the South Devon Rail-way; Brunel and the Broad Gauge; Samuda, and the Atmos-pheric', though Lady Watson, who lived there, complained of the amount of smoke given out by the local engines.

On 17 December two more trains in each direction between Exeter and Teignmouth were transferred to atmospheric work-ing, and the express each way. Some trains to Newton were also atmospherically worked from this date until on 10 January 1848 most passengers and goods traffic to Newton was put on atmos-pheric, with seven up and six down weekday passenger trains that were allowed 55 minutes for the journey, with four stops. Three down and two up night trains were locomotive-hauled to save extra working of the stationary engines.

The breakdown that had occurred during the frost annoyed

a lot of people, many of whom lost confidence in the system because they could not see how the trouble was to be cured. The directors, however, were saying that results justified pushing on to Plymouth. The frost ended, the services improved, and at the shareholders' meeting on 26 February, the vice-chairman quoted figures for 884 atmospheric trains, of which 790 had gained or been on time, another 70 not more than five minutes late, 14 six to ten minutes late, and 10 over ten minutes late.* He added that there were no grounds for asserting that the mechanical working of the system had failed, and complained that when an atmospheric train was delayed by a steam-hauled connection at either end of the line, the system got the blame.

On 23 February all trains were transferred to atmospheric working. The first was the 4 a.m. mail, the last the midnight goods, so that the engines were now working for twenty hours a day. The short trains hitherto run between Exeter and Teignmouth were now extended to Newton. Crossing was done at Teignmouth, though on 9 March the 6.20 a.m. heavy fish train from Totnes was late after climbing Dainton, and it was decided to cross it with the 7.50 down at Starcross, the engine there exhausting the tube from Dawlish to Turf and bringing both trains successfully to the crossing.

At the February shareholders' meeting, at which Ellis, deputy-chairman of the Midland Railway, insisted that atmospheric working should not be extended beyond Totnes, Brunel hoped soon to overcome his difficulties, when 'the working of the Atmospheric will . . . become the subject of actual experiment, and its value be practically tested'. He thought atmospheric working would be extended to Totnes in three or four months, and reported that the engine-house at Dainton† was finished, with preparations being made to erect the engines, and that the tube was being laid beyond Newton.

* These figures did not, of course, cover trains locomotive-hauled from the start.

† Dainton engine-house was at the far end of the tunnel on the down side. It was built with a siding rising in front of it, from which trucks could have tipped coal into its stores.

After this the line seems to have worked reliably through February, March, and (except on one day) April. Early in 1849 the board said of this period : 'At that time the expense of working was very great, although in some other respects (especially as regards punctuality in working the trains) the results were satisfactory', but that Brunel had told them he hoped for great reductions when certain mechanical difficulties had been overcome. In April Rattery engine-house beyond Totnes was begun.

On 5 May locomotive working was extended from Totnes to Laira Green outside Plymouth, and simultaneously fares were raised on the whole line. Ten up and eleven down trains started running (five on Sunday), some, however, only between Exeter and Teignmouth or Newton. At Newton, of course, trains to and from Totnes and Plymouth had to exchange motive power. The chairman—one must remember that his views did not entirely correspond with those of many members of his board—was hopeful. 'I think the County of Devon ought to be proud that the directors of the South Devon Railway have chosen, by the advice of their Engineer, that system of traction which, I believe, will confer vast benefit upon the world at large (enthusiastic cheering). Sufficient for the present that we have brought it to a point, which has proved eminently successful. We have occasionally heard of a few defects, but they do not exceed those of the ordinary system—I believe it will be found as regular, with some trivial exceptions traceable to causes, perfectly remedial, and that we have so far succeeded that we have no reason to doubt of the ultimate success of the atmospheric system' (great applause).

The first three weeks of May brought some delays, and an undercurrent of criticism now shows itself, though in early June a newspaper correspondent describes them as no worse than usual on steam lines. Those out to criticise, criticised everything; but ordinary indications show that the service was reasonably reliable. Later, shareholders were told that between 11 May and 27 July, 1,628 atmospheric trains had been run, with a total gain in time of $55\frac{1}{2}$ hours, and a loss of $73\frac{3}{4}$. Much of the trouble was that when a train failed, it so often needed rescue by a locomotive. If this happened, delays to the service were serious for some hours, and the rescue was obvious to all, and looked bad. However, on the steam-worked section between Newton and Totnes some third-class coaches had to be taken off trains, because locomotives were finding the inclines too much for them, and in July, with the big Boulton & Watt engines at Dainton almost ready (they had originally been built for the Epsom extension) it seemed likely that the line could be opened to Totnes without waiting for engines to be installed there. However, high costs still continued, though Brunel told the board that many difficulties were not the fault of the system. The insufficient power of Maudslay's engines at Dawlish was one.

All the same, valve decay was causing trouble. In August Brunel was to write that within the last few months, but especially in the dry weather of May and June, a considerable extent of valve had failed by the leather tearing at the joint between the plates. The leather first cracked, causing leakage especially in dry weather, and then tore. An example of real trouble from this cause, maliciously told by *Woolmer's Gazette*, occurred on 4 August, when a goods train tore the valve between Dawlish and Teignmouth. The following down train ran well from Exeter to Dawlish, but afterwards got stuck near a tunnel. The train and engine staff had to push it clear of the damaged valve, which was then plugged with a railwayman's cape and coat, to enable it to get away. One eyewitness of the line at this time, Edward Pearse, said holes were bored in the tube to admit water, which the piston would then splash on to the underside of the valve to help keep it moist. The valve was tearing over long sections, and sets us something of a problem, for nothing comparable occurred on the other lines. Why did this trouble occur on the South Devon?

There seem to have been several causes. When the trouble began to occur extensively, Samuda told Brunel that after delivery the valve had been kept for a long time in its packing cases and that, exposed to damp, the iron had started to rust before the valve had been installed. Samuda had delivered seven miles of valve by end-June 1845, and another 14 miles by September. It is probable, therefore, that it was kept in cases for about a year before being fitted on the Exeter–Dawlish section, and between nineteen and twenty-four months on the Dawlish–Newton section, apart from some time after it had been installed but before the first test trains ran. Nothing like this delay occurred on any other line.

Another was the sea air. Most of the South Devon line was on or near the coast, exposed to the natural humidity of the air and from time to time to westerly gales also, whereas the Dalkey, the only other atmospheric railway near the sea, was much more protected. Salt air makes no particular difference to leather, but causes iron to rust much more quickly, especially when in contact with saturated leather on one side and air on the other. Then it is the iron in contact with the leather that rusts quickest. This removal of metal would mean that rivets fastening the iron plates to the leather, and one layer of leather to the other, would become loose, and as play developed the valve would tear more readily and leakage increase.

A third possible factor is the composition used on the valve. On the Dalkey and in early days on the Croydon this was a mixture of beeswax and tallow, which is a crude form of an anti-corrosion mixture (PX 11) used today in the aircraft industry. On the other hand, the lime soap used for at any rate part of the South Devon's life could have accelerated corrosion.

These are the probable causes : they all affected the iron, not the leather. There are also indications, however, of decay in some of the leather used, but one cannot assign a cause for this without knowing much more about the particular leather. The main trouble, however, was tearing as a result of removal of metal, which loosened the fastenings of the valve and made it less able to withstand the shock of the piston passing along it.

Oddly, it was a letter complaining of 'recent irregularities' in the working of the atmospheric line which caused the board on 23 May to appoint a sub-committee of Gill and two others to investigate. This leads one to think that the actual operating cannot have been too bad. They reported on 20 June. Engines and telegraph were not mentioned, the trouble was the valve: 'there was an unexpected, rapid, and continuing destruction going on in the leather' and this involved 'the serious weekly expense in repairs . . . as well as the loss occasioned by its defective state in the general working of the Line'. Between October 1847 and 30 June 1848, 2¾ miles of valve had to be renewed. Valve renewals were therefore rather over 10 per cent of the total length of line in use: the cost was 32s 6d per 20 ft length, £1,018 17s 6d in all. The board decided that Samuda was to be debited with the whole cost of valve repairs, which they could do for twelve months after public working began under their agreement, that further payments to him should be withheld, and that Brunel should report in writing 'upon the probability of overcoming by any means the difficulties that have been experienced in reference to the construction and working of the present Longitudinal Valve'. He was also asked to arrange with Boulton & Watt for the completion and then disposal of the engines on order, it now being certain that the atmospheric would not be extended beyond Totnes.

As on 18 July nothing had been heard from Brunel, a deputation was sent to interview him; they did so, and received his written report later. In it he said: 'It is quite possible that a valve made in the same manner as at present, if properly attended to from the first, and with our present experience, might not be subject to this destruction, and Mr Samuda states such is the case at Dalkey, but I do not think I could rely on the result. By painting, but better still, by zincing or galvanising the iron plates, and making them overlap a short distance, both the chemical and the mechanical action of the plate upon the leather seems to be prevented, and I believe, therefore, that this evil may be remedied at a small increased cost in any new or repaired valve that may be laid down; but of the existing valve I can say no more than I have done. It is not in good working condition, and I see no immediate prospect of it being rendered so.' If the valve were renewed, and some money spent on the engines, the costs of working would be very much reduced—but renewal would take a year, and until then they would continue. His suggestions were sound, and if they had been adopted, as far as we can tell the valve would have remained sound.

Having digested Brunel's report, and seen Samuda, the sub-committee met the full board on 28 and 29 August. They reported what Brunel had said about the valve, and his opinion that unless Samuda would renew it, and then guarantee it for a long period, 'I fear that the Company would not be justified in taking that upon themselves, or incurring the expense attending the alteration of the engines'. He still thought, however, that the apparatus would be found 'applicable and efficient' to assist trains on the four inclines, and had suggested that as the engines and tube were nearly ready at Dainton, they should be tried there, if Samuda would maintain the valve. Before the board also was Samuda's offer to improve and maintain the valve for twelve months (though he refused to work the line), with an explanation of what he proposed to do, and also Pearson's report on the possibilities of reducing working expenses.

Gill wanted to accept Samuda's proposals, so establishing his liability; to make a contribution towards the cost of perfecting the valve and engines, and to seek the working economies thought possible by Brunel and Pearson. He could not get a seconder. The board decided that atmospheric working at the company's cost should stop after Saturday 9 September 'until the Patentees and Mr Samuda shall have adopted some means to the satisfaction of the Directors for relieving the Company from the loss consequent upon working under such disadvantages'. Facilities would be given for the patentees and Samuda to restore the valve and make experiments, but by 6 September these must agree to undertake the expenses of working the line at a reasonable and defined cost per train during the alterations, should they desire atmospheric working to continue while they were being made.*

---

* In fact, locomotive working was brought forward, and began on Wednesday 6 September.

As a last encouragement they agreed that the South Devon would contribute to any improvement if the atmospheric system could be beneficially resumed. A shareholders' meeting, which lasted noisily for four hours, was held on 31 August. Bravely, Samuda was present, to listen with Gill to the jibes of those who had so loudly cheered the atmospheric only a few months before. There was loud applause when Mr Seccombe of the Bristol & Exeter called him 'as wild a visionary as ever existed', and Ellis of the Midland said his company was 'exceedingly disgusted with that atmospheric bauble'. In the following year, when his own chairman George Hudson was exposed, Ellis was to find himself similarly placed to Thomas Gill.

Meanwhile there is no indication that the service had collapsed. On 2 August the London express arrived behind time at Exeter, and also two detachments of troops to be taken to Plymouth. The first train was sent off at 2.30 and arrived at Newton in 38 minutes. Another followed, and then the express, now an hour late. At Newton, three trains were then made up and dispatched back in 36 minutes, followed by the up mail. These extra workings, in addition to the normal service, on a single line, do not show disorganisation. Indeed the *Railway Chronicle*, under the signature 'Eye Witness' said: 'every observer, however casual, could not have failed to perceive that a great improvement in the working was gradually taking place from week to week; and that for the last three months an irregularity of even a few minutes was difficult to point out'. The writer may have been biased, but he can hardly be altogether wrong.

On 3 August about 80 workmen of the atmospheric department had supper together at the Newfoundland Inn, Newton, to celebrate the opening of the new workshops there. James Pearson was in the chair, and said he was confident that the atmospheric system had got over its chief difficulties. 'Success to the atmospheric system' was drunk, and the healths of Brunel and Samuda down to the local foremen. Indeed, it must have seemed to the men that they were getting the valve trouble right, for only ten days before closure sections of a new and improved valve using rubber were being fitted at Dawlish, one of several experiments with new designs.

It is notable that closure was orderly, the last train being the usual midnight goods. The end caused consternation among the staff, and was a nine days' wonder for the passengers. As is always the case with failure, those who had always known it would not work multiplied, and there were bitter attacks on Brunel and the directors. But some were kinder. The *Western Times*' Teignmouth correspondent wrote: 'A whole host of valve stoppers set out for home . . . and we thought their lament something like the following:

> 'Farewell the tranquil mind—farewell content!
> Farewell, ye pistons, pipes, and valves, and all!
> Farewell extensive sheds, and the fat grease
> That makes the valves adhesive. All farewell!
> Adieu, great air-exhausting engine-houses!
> The Atmospheric occupation's gone'.

A week later the paper told its readers that 'the engine-houses already present a melancholy aspect, they are dark at night and silent by day', and 'the change did not occur without an expression of deep regret on the part of a large number of persons who have been accustomed to the atmospheric traction. Comparative ease of motion, and a greater sense of security, had led many travellers on the line to look with increasing interest towards the extension of the system to Totnes'. And the *Gazette*, which had attacked the atmospheric throughout, now hedged, and said it was important that the engine-houses should not be knocked down in a hurry. In fact, for the time being everything was left in place.

Some trains were now removed from the service, but delays were not eliminated. Up and down the line there must have been some who smiled to hear that on 18 September a special excursion from Exeter to Plymouth had two half-hour delays on the way down and one of an hour on the way back.

Gill had not agreed with the board's decision, and in the

autumn he insisted on retiring from the chairmanship in order that he could put his views before the shareholders, and was succeeded by the vice-chairman, Woollcombe. Gill published a pamphlet, the text of which he refused to show the board before issue, that suggested running the atmospheric as far as Totnes for one more year at a cost he reckoned as £6,000, if possible by an agreement with Samuda to work the line, to test its performance on the hilly sections between Newton and Totnes, and to establish what its working costs really were, to see if a certain loss of £300,000 could be avoided. He called a meeting in Bristol which requested a full shareholders' meeting. The board thought his pamphlet 'calculated to produce erroneous impressions on the minds of the Proprietors', and circulated a printed reply. In January 1849 the shareholders listened to Gill, who was now pushing Clarke and Varley's system, the patentees of which, he said, were willing to put up £10,000 for experiments on two miles of line, and, if they succeeded, to contract to work the South Devon at 1s a train-mile. But only 1,875 shares were prepared to encourage him, even to the extent of appointing a committee of shareholders to inquire into the affairs of the company, including methods of traction; 5,900 shares had had enough.

Settlements were made with the trustees and Samuda, but except for the sale of a quantity of 22 in tube, and arrangements to dispose of the engines on order from Boulton & Watt and Harvey's of Hayle, the existing plant was left on site until May 1849, when Brunel was asked whether he thought there was still a chance that it might be needed. Clearly there was not, and in June the sale of engine-houses, engines, tubes, and valve leather began, though the engines at Exeter, Countess Wear, Turf, Starcross, Teignmouth, Newton, and Dainton had been mortgaged to the Devon & Cornwall Bank until November 1852, and were not sold until after that.

When the service ended, engines had been installed at Dainton, but probably not worked. At Totnes the boilers were in, and 'machinery', perhaps the air-pumps; at Torre nothing. The

SOUTH DEVON RAILWAY.
TO BUILDERS, MECHANICAL ENGINEERS,
AND OTHERS.

THE WHOLE OF THE

BUILDING
MATERIALS
OF THE

ENGINE-HOUSES,

At TEIGNMOUTH, and near the SUMMER-HOUSE, about midway between NEWTON and TEIGNMOUTH,

WILL BE SOLD BY

AUCTION,

On **MONDAY**, the 3rd of **SEPTEMBER**, 1855,

IN THE FOLLOWING LOTS,

AT THE TEIGNMOUTH ENGINE-HOUSE,

SALE TO COMMENCE AT TWO o'CLOCK TO THE MINUTE.

Lot 1.—The whole of the Materials of the Chimney and Tower (which is beautifully Built in the Italian Style of Architecture); comprising about 320 Perch of Lime Stone; 420 Superficial Feet of Ashler Work; 800 ditto of Rusticated ditto, with Circular-Headed Doorway; Framed Door and Jambs; Four 3-Light Windows; 84 Feet run of enriched Bath Stone Cornice; Four 3-Light Bath Stone Turret Windows; 56 Feet Bath Stone Moulded Story Band; the Italian Tile Roofing, including the Timbers; 9; Rod Standard Brickwork; Iron Fire Door and Frame; and 115 Slate Steps and Risers; Landing; Half and Quarter Spaces; Iron Work; &c.

ENGINE HOUSE.

Lot 2.—The whole of the Timbers of Roof, including the Boarding and Italian Tile, about 11 Square.

Lot 3.—The whole of the Lime Stone Walls, about 140 Perch, with Two Circular-Headed Ashler Doorways, and Framed Doors; Ashler Plinths; Rusticated Pilasters; Bath Stone Cornice and Moulded String-Courses; Two Double Circular-Headed Windows and Jambs, including Sashes.

Lot 4.—The whole of the Brick and Stone Walls of the Interior; also, the Granite Steps and Blocks.

BOILER HOUSE.

Lot 5.—The whole of the Timbers of Roof, including the Italian Tile, about 23 Square.

Lot 6.—The Lead, at per Cwt.

Lot 7.—The whole of the Lime Stone Walls, with the Ashler Plinths, Three Circular-Headed Doorways, with Framed Doors and Jambs; Three Circular-Headed Transoms, Bath Stone Windows, with Sashes; Two Circular ditto, ditto.

AT THE SUMMER-HOUSE ENGINE-HOUSE,

SITUATED ON THE LINE BETWEEN TEIGNMOUTH AND NEWTON,

SALE TO COMMENCE AT FIVE o'CLOCK TO THE MINUTE.

ENGINE HOUSE.

Lot 1.—The whole of the Timbers and Boarding of Roof, including the Italian Tile, about 17 Square.

Lot 3.—The whole of the Lime Stone Walls, about 300 Perch, a portion of which is Ashler Work; Two Bath Stone Window Frames; Two Semi-Head ditto; Three Pair Folding Doors and Frames; &c.; &c.

Lot 4.—A Double Flight of 26 Granite Steps, and Landing, with Iron Hand Rails, Baluster, and Stone Walling.

Lot 5.—The whole of the Brick and Stone Walls of the Interior; also, the York Stone Landings, Bath Stone Blocks, &c.

BOILER HOUSE.

Lot 6.—The whole of the Timbers of Roof, including the Italian Tile, about 17 Square; also, the Deal Staircase and Platform.

Lot 7.—The Lime Stone Walls about 150 Perch; 200 Feet Ashler Work; Three Circular-Headed Door Frames and Doors; Seven Windows and Frames; 120 Feet run Bath Stone Moulded Story Band, &c., &c.

Lot 9.—The Chimney, about 14 Rod Standard Brickwork; 200 Superficial Feet Lime Stone—Base Part Ashler, 44 Feet run Moulded Bath Stone Band; 56 Feet Bath Stone Block Cornice; Italian Tile Coping; &c.; &c.

Lot 10.—**TWO large AIR PUMPS**, with Pistons, Pump Rods, large Air Chamber, and Connecting Pipes and Valves, Four Bearing Girders, &c.

THE PUMPS WERE MADE BY MESSRS. MAUDSLEY, SONS AND FIELD, AND ARE 4 INCHES IN DIAMETER WITH 4 FEET STROKE.

The whole of these Buildings have been recently erected, in the Italian style of Architecture, with the best Materials and Workmanship, and, as every Lot will be Sold to the best Bidder, it offers an opportunity rarely to be met with. Lot 1, of the Teignmouth Property, from its pure Italian style of Architecture and superior Materials, is particularly adapted for any Gentleman who is about to erect an Observatory, or any Building of that Character.

☞ There is a RAILWAY SIDING to this BUILDING, and the usual Accommodation will be afforded to Purchasers for the use thereof.

Any further Information may be obtained of MESSRS. DYMOND and SONS, Surveyors, EXETER.

Wm. WILLS, Auctioneer, Exeter.

NORTON, PRINTER AND STATIONER, &c., 6, DRAKES, SOUTH STREET, EXETER.

Notice of sale for Teignmouth and Summerhouse engine-houses on the
South Devon

engines for Rattery had been delivered to Totnes by Harvey's of Hayle, but had not been installed. Today engine-houses, shells without chimneys, stand beside the line at Exeter, Starcross, Totnes, and Torre, and portions of others remain; there is a section of 22 in tube in the Science Museum; and the publishers of this book work in a station that once saw the arrival and departure of the silent trains.

The total expenditure on the atmospheric line seems to have been £433,991, made up as follows:

	£	s	d
Tubes	194,503	10	10
Continuous valve and fastenings	27,976	9	1
Composition for valve	9,219	12	5
Section valves, starting gear etc.	3,846	10	7
Apparatus	18,688	4	9
Piston gear	2,786	1	9
Machinery, Tools etc.	1,684	10	4
Newton workshop	203	8	0
Engine-houses	48,610	19	10
Engines and vacuum pumps ...	117,721	17	1
Patent right	8,750	0	0
	£433,991	4	8

The amount recovered seems to have been about £81,000, leaving a debit of about £353,000.

The payments to engine-makers were approximately:

	£	s	d
Boulton & Watt	75,319	14	1
G. & J. Rennie	18,510	11	0
Harvey & Co.	12,767	0	0
Maudslay, Son & Field	11,124	11	11

Relations with Samuda must have remained good, for in 1851 we find his firm building thirty coal trucks for the South Devon, and in 1853 they bought back some of the big engines: one from Newton, two each from Summerhouse and Dawlish, a small one from Dawlish, and an air vessel from Dainton. In 1856 they were making brake vans.

It is very difficult to assess correctly the reason for the atmospheric failure of the South Devon, because so much is still unknown. What can be said with some confidence is that, if we eliminate delays due to locomotive late running on either side, the train service was not noticeably worse, and was probably about the same, as on the steam lines.

The basic trouble was that, as on the Croydon, the system was under-powered. Brunel had originally chosen 13 in tubes for the Exeter–Newton section and had then substituted 15 in. There is evidence that in the last three months of service he was preparing to change over to 22 in. A newspaper report of 1 July says the company is 'laying down tubes of larger calibre on the line in the room of those already in operation. Every afternoon a train starts from Exeter at 3.15, to convey portions of the new tubes to the different depots', and at the shareholders' meeting on 31 August there is a reference to thousands of 15 in tubes being broken up and recast into 22 in.

This under-powering was due in the first place to the collective misjudgement of Samuda, Cubitt, and Brunel, that a single atmospheric line was almost as good as double locomotive lines. From Samuda's point of view, this was a precondition of success for his system, for the construction cost of double-track atmospheric lines would have been prohibitive. But a single line limited the number of trains that could be run, and so added to their weight. For instance, Brunel had envisaged light, frequent goods trains. But heavy trains, goods and express, arrived at Exeter or Newton, and had to be run to the limit of weight before being delayed by splitting in two. In the three weeks before the final closure of the system, the average weekly train mileage had been 3,140; in the three following weeks it was 2,228. This was to some extent the result of a reduced service, but much more to heavier trains being run. From the company's point of view, they were carrying nearly the same traffic and taking nearly the same money at less cost.

As we saw, Brunel was working a 15 in tube with pairs of 41½ hp engines designed for one of 13in. But, if one can generalise from the evidence available on the Boulton & Watt engines to the others also, the air pumps were too small. The $41\frac{1}{2}$ hp Boulton & Watts should have driven a 72 in pump instead of one of 51 in. This meant that the engines had to run faster than designed to make up for lack of capacity, and hence were less efficient. Gill said that the engines designed to pump at 18 to 20 strokes a minute had to be run at 25 to 30 or even more.

Heavy trains worked over too small a tube meant vacuums higher than the normal 15–16 in; as on the Croydon, the South Devon often worked at over 20. This compelled the engines to work harder, and probably always coupled, for leakage increased rapidly after about 15 in of vacuum had been obtained, even with the valve in good condition.

In hot weather, when the temperature of the air in the main and connecting tubes rose, that in the pumps would rise also, and this may well have led to increased leakage through their packing. The engines also had to work longer than foreseen, because of the incomplete installation of the telegraph in the engine houses, for without accurate information on late trains, enginemen had to pump by time-table, keeping their engines going until the trains arrived.

Engines running faster, longer, and usually coupled meant high coal consumption and so high working costs. Brunel, as we have seen, blamed the engines, but in a way that avoided saying what was really happening. His report of 19 August 1848 said that the engine makers had prepared their own designs, and Samuda had superintended manufacture. No engines had yet worked economically, and some were very extravagant. 'The apparent causes of this excess are various in the different engines, but all resulting more or less apparently from the want of experience in this particular application of power, and from the circumstance of the form of the engine being somewhat novel, and involving slight differences in the proportion and arrangement of the parts; and the consumption being greater than was calculated upon, it has been obtained with a more wasteful expenditure of fuel.' All the same, Pearson and his men had been

getting costs down as experience of working grew. Gill, of course
a biased witness, said that from the beginning of March 1848,
just after all trains had gone over to atmospheric working, to 2
August, when the telegraph was completed, coal consumption
had fallen from about 40 to about 30 tons a day, and that from
2 August it fell further to 28 tons at the time of closure.

The valve has taken all the blame for the failure of atmospheric working on the South Devon. Certainly portions tore
away due to rusting and, in spite of using various types of composition, it hardened in frost. The result was not indeed any
serious collapse of train services, but heavy spending to maintain
them, on replacing lengths of valve and on the manpower
necessary to keep the leather pliable and airtight.

Again, Brunel had enormously underestimated his installation
costs, and so the amount of capital necessary and the interest
that had to be earned to service it. His figure, we may remember,
was £190,000 for the whole line to Plymouth, with tube at
£3,300 a mile and engine-houses complete with their engines at
£5,100 each. He spent about twice that on the line to Totnes.
After allowing for his mistake in ordering 13 in tube, what was
laid cost about £6,400 a mile and the engines and pumps from
£5,500 upwards for each house.

Finally, to the spending on operation and maintenance, and
on servicing capital, had to be added that on providing locomotives to work trains forward from Newton to Totnes and later
Plymouth, and stand-bys in case of atmospheric failure. This
level of spending in the end forced the directors and shareholders
to their decision. The figures given to the 31 August meeting
were 3s 1½d per train mile for the atmospheric and 2s 6d for
the locomotive-worked section, each being higher because of the
other. Based on the first half of 1848, these were to some extent
unfair to the atmospheric, for they included costs of engine
repairs, telegraph installations and valve replacements that were
probably abnormal, and on the locomotive side several months
of very expensive working between Newton and Totnes only.
Brunel, however, did not think he could get the figure for the

atmospheric working below 2s 0d within twelve months; Pearson maintained that after a better valve had been fitted, it could be brought down to 1s 3½d.

What had happened was the inevitable result of Samuda's advocacy of intensive single-track working without realising that it was impossible to equalise train weights on a line so closely linked with its neighbour as the South Devon, of Brunel's under-estimates and failure to get the telegraph installed earlier, and of the board's decision not to carry the atmospheric beyond Totnes. Underlying these were the technical facts; the change of tube size too late to alter the engines, pumps too small, valve leakage, and the rusting of the iron parts of the valve, causing more leak-age and frequent tearing.

The only solution lay in new valve, bigger tubes and larger engines and pumps which would allow ordinary trains to be worked at low vacuums and give a reserve of power for those that were heavier: indeed, in a new railway. It was an impossible price to pay.

Chemin de fer atmosphérique. — Vue des machines pneumatiques.

XXI.   *Inside Saint Germain engine-house*

XXII. *The experimental passenger tube line built in the Crystal Palace grounds in 1864*

CHAPTER ELEVEN

THE SAINT GERMAIN LINE

THE movement in favour of atmospheric railways began in France in 1842, when Samuda's pamphlet was translated by du Perron. In the autumn M. Teisserenc de Bort was sent over to England at the request of the French ambassador. He made tests at Wormwood Scrubs in November, and on his return reported in March 1843 to the Minister of Public Works. What he said was favourable to the system. 'Its use,' he concluded, 'will do away with the useless weight of the locomotive or, where stationary engines are used, with that of the cables.' A debate with two aspects now began: should the atmospheric system be adopted on any French lines, and, if so, should that of Clegg and Samuda be chosen, or one of the French systems which were modifications of it?

To settle the first question a second mission was sent to England, led by the Ponts et Chaussées engineer M. Mallet, Inspector-General of Public Works. He visited the Dalkey line, and in turn reported favourably and in detail, ending with a recommendation that trials should be made to settle the value of the system for a line with steep gradients, and also how far it was applicable to a normal railway. Now in France Jules Petiet, engineer of the Compagnie de Paris à Versailles, took up the same position as Robert Stephenson in England. He went critically through Mallet's report, contesting it point by point. He was especially critical of the likely construction costs, even for a single-track line, thought that the stationary engines wasted a great deal of power, and that it was impossible to relate fuel costs to the effort demanded. He therefore ruled the system out for long railways, but thought there was a use for it to surmount steep gradients on mountain lines.

The main French system was Hallette's, which used two small tubes filled with compressed air to close the slot in the tube instead of Clegg and Samuda's leather valve. He built a model in his engineering works at Arras and obtained Press support and that of the scientific savant M. Arago. However, investigations concluded that although his system did reduce leakage, it

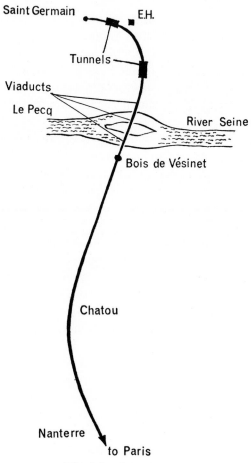

The Saint Germain line

had great disadvantages, and when a line was built, the English system was used on it.

On 8 July 1844 those who thought atmospheric railways had real possibilities obtained from the Government an Act authorising a thorough test of the system, and granting 1,800,000 francs* towards it. The object was to establish whether an atmospheric line could 'satisfy all the movements which make up the ordinary operation of a railway'. The first tests were prescribed over a distance of two kilometres, but in the end a line of about 16 km was envisaged, with varying gradients. The testing company would be free to use either Hallette's or Clegg and Samuda's system.

There were three main candidates for the subsidy. One project was for a line on the Satory plateau between Versailles and Saint Cyr; another to lengthen the Sceaux line between Bourg la Reine and Orsay; the third for a railway on the bank of the Ourcq Canal between La Villette and Sevran. Finally, after much argument about these, the Ponts et Chaussées chose a fourth, and gave the subsidy to the Compagnie du Chemin de Fer de Paris à Saint Germain. This company had been founded in 1835, the first in Paris, and had opened its line as far as Le Pecq, at the foot of the slope leading up to the castle and the town, on 26 August 1837. With the permissible gradients of the time it was considered impossible to take a locomotive line up to the town, and passengers therefore travelled between Saint Germain and Le Pecq by horse omnibus. The town felt the disadvantages of its situation, especially after the Paris–Rouen railway had been opened, and itself offered 200,000 francs of additional subsidy. The place had long been considered for a trial of the atmospheric system : Clegg had thought of establishing himself there in 1839, Samuda made proposals in 1843, and Vignoles said that it was the best place in France for a trial, for it had the double advantage of a steep gradient and the likelihood of a dense and important traffic.

The subsidy meant that the extension offered many advantages

* About £90,000 in contemporary English money.

and few risks to the Saint Germain company. However, the Rouen company, which already served the plateau, was very annoyed, and it inspired Press criticisms and made a protest to the Council of State. 'Not only', wrote the *Journal des Chemins de Fer* of 26 October 1844, 'is the Saint Germain company given permission to lengthen its line to the terrace of the castle, but it is also presented as a pure gift with half the sum that it would have to spend in any case'. It concluded: 'The Chambers have voted an encouragement for the atmospheric system and not a subsidy for the Saint Germain railway.' However, the Council of State rejected the protest, and the administration of the royal domain authorised the crossing of the Forest of Saint Germain.

These happenings held back the presentation of the proposal to a shareholders' meeting until November 1845, when a report was made by the Chairman of the Board, Isaac Pereire. He proposed to use the new system from Nanterre (about $5\frac{1}{2}$ miles from Saint Germain) along one track of the existing line. At Le Pecq the atmospheric track would leave the old one, cross the Seine by bridges and so rise 174 feet to the terrace by a viaduct and tunnels on a gradient of about 1 in 29. There would be three engine-houses, at Nanterre, Chatou, and Saint Germain, with coupled engines together producing 100, 200, and 400 hp respectively. Tube of 14 in diameter would be used on the Nanterre–Vésinet Wood section, and of 25 in on the final steeply-graded track to the castle. The cost was estimated at 4 million francs. To cover the difference between this sum and the subsidy the company had in March 1845 obtained authority to increase its capital by issuing new shares. Pereire showed that the operation would be viable, taking account of the ending of the subsidy given to the omnibus service between Le Pecq and Saint Germain.

The main works were quickly built by the engineer in charge, Eugène Flachat; the double bridges over the Seine, the great viaduct of twenty arches that ran about 60 ft above the valley, and the two tunnels separated by a cutting. But the atmospheric

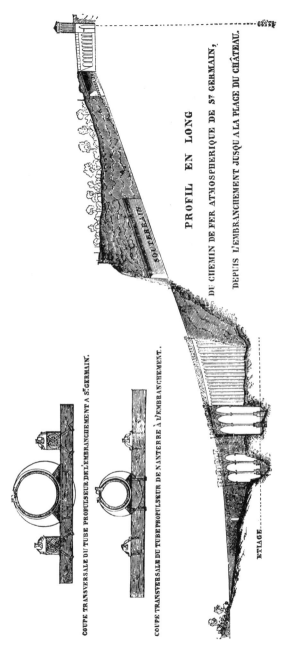

COUPE TRANSVERSALE DU TUBE PROPULSEUR DE L'EMBRANCHEMENT A S.ᵗ GERMAIN.

COUPE TRANSVERSALE DU TUBE PROPULSEUR DE NANTERRE À L'EMBRANCHEMENT.

PROFIL EN LONG

DU CHEMIN DE FER ATMOSPHERIQUE DE Sᵀ GERMAIN,

DEPUIS L'EMBRANCHEMENT JUSQU'A LA PLACE DU CHÂTEAU.

SOUTERRAIN

ETIAGE

Profile of the Saint Germain line and sections of the tubes, only the larger of which was installed
Changes from this early sketch were made in the line as constructed

apparatus for which Joseph Samuda was consulting engineer
took longer, for the company had to contend with the same
delays in delivery that plagued their English opposite numbers.
Hallette of Arras, Meyer of Mulhouse and the Seraing works
were building the stationary engines, Cail the boilers, Chagot et
Brunet the tubes: they ought to have been delivered between
June 1845 and March 1846, though most did not appear until
1847. The works did not hurry, for by now they were certain
no further orders would be forthcoming, but later the company
demanded and obtained compensation.

The delays had an unintended result. The gradient between
Le Pecq and Saint Germain was much steeper than normally
authorised for locomotives, but Flachat, under the pretext that
it was needed for transporting construction materials, built in
the company's workshops the locomotive *L'Hercule*. With six-
coupled wheels of $47\frac{1}{4}$ in diameter and 15 in cylinders, this
engine succeeded in climbing the incline with a working load.
The *Journal des Chemins de Fer* observed that the company
and its engineer 'are sure at least that if the atmospheric railway
does not succeed or if it produced working difficulties, the track
built to test it could usefully be worked by ordinary engines in
an economical way'. With *L'Hercule* went one of the atmospheric's claimed advantages: its use on steep gradients not work-
able by locomotives.

The use of *L'Hercule* enabled French engineers to demonstrate
that gradients much steeper than those still imposed on companies by the Public Works administration could be worked by
locomotives. Costs were mounting on the Saint Germain line—
they reached six millions—and that company would probably
have liked to get out of its obligations, for, wrote the *Journal des
Chemins de Fer* on 27 June 1846, 'all the world is now convinced that the system cannot support the promises made in its
name, when one knows without doubt that the costs of first construction are much higher than that of the ordinary railway,
that its installation and maintenance are more expensive, that
its operation is inconvenient and does not lend itself to a service

at any time, like a locomotive line'. However, a Commission presided over by M. Arago gave permission for the section between Nanterre and Bois de Vésinet not to be completed, though the engines had been installed at Nanterre and Chatou. Therefore the only section to be finished was that between Bois de Vésinet and Saint Germain by way of Le Pecq, a distance of 1⅜ miles, using the one engine house at Saint Germain, equipped with Hallette's engines.

The first tests took place in January 1847. During these, trains of eleven carriages excluding the piston carriage, and weighing up to 62¾ tons, were taken up. The line opened unobtrusively, on 24 April. A four-wheeled piston carriage was used, with a piston counterweighted not with lead but with a 6 ft wooden cylinder. There was no heater. On the arrival of the Paris train at Bois de Vésinet, the locomotive was taken off, and the train shunted up to be coupled to the piston carriage, waiting where the tube began. The piston lay in a separate short tube, linked past a valve with the main tube. When the starting signal was given, the valve was opened, and the piston carriage gained sufficient momentum to pass the main valve and into the tube itself. Communication with the Saint Germain engines was by electric telegraph. The slope was usually climbed at about 25 mph in three or four minutes. At the top the tube ended, and the train then coasted the last 181 yd into the station, spring buffers of vulcanised rubber being provided in case of brake failure.

In Saint Germain station trains were broken and remade using an atmospheric capstan and also a hydraulic traverser which could transfer vehicles from one track to another. For the return journey the piston was swung to one side of the piston carriage by two men and fastened. The capstan was then used to pull the train by rope to the top of the slope, when it ran by gravity, being controlled by its brakes. Many tests had been made to make sure that this method was safe. In one of them a single carriage loaded with weights equal to forty passengers had been sent down the slope without brakes, and only achieved 49 mph. When the train arrived at Bois de Vésinet, the piston carriage was taken off the train and run on to a siding. There the piston was lowered, and it was ready to take the next train up.

The two horizontal 200 hp Saint Germain engines were linked to the air pumps by a pinion working on an enormous 26 ft gear-wheel. These pumps were very large, with four 81 in cylinders. Auxiliary engines were provided, presumably to work the condenser and cold water pumps as on the South Devon Railway. Five strokes of the steam engine produced one of the pump, and an indicator was provided to count the strokes. The number necessary to work a train up being known, the engine-man therefore knew when to stop pumping. The longitudinal valve was of the Dalkey type, but a different mixture seems to have been used for the composition, of seal oil, wax, rubber, and clay.

Before the line was opened there was a good deal of excitement. In February 1847 *Le Moniteur Universel* wrote a good purple passage: 'Imagine an immense building of stone and brick dominating the forest plain . . . with its tall chimneys like obelisks, then below furnaces vast as imagination can alone conjecture, titanic fires vomiting flame by every mouth, immense cylinders working horizontally their gigantesque iron trees, a noise which exceeds that of the fire-pumps we know, and in the middle of this deafening noise, of these wheels large as triumphal arches, of chains rolling themselves up, of levers falling and lifting with a supernatural force, calm and attentive engineers, directing all by thought, starting or stopping without trouble the most impetuous movements of the terrible machine, this apparatus which launches into space or draws towards it these rolling masses by the application of atmospheric air.' There was, however, agreement that the motion of the atmospheric train was pleasantly smooth and free from oscillation, and Isaac Pereire had good hopes: 'Everyone', he told the shareholders in March 1847, 'will wish to make this marvellous climb, which ends in the parterre of the castle of Saint Germain.'

But beauty, approval, curiosity, and safety were not all: the line had to pay. The estimate had been considerably exceeded, the final cost reaching 6,137,633 francs (about £300,000). Not all was attributable to the atmospheric system. Expenditure included interest paid to shareholders owing to the delay in opening the line, in turn due to delays in delivery of materials; modifications made as a result of experience on the London & Croydon; and the adding of a second track accessible to locomotives in case of atmospheric failure.

The working expenses were also high to begin with, but a great effort was made to economise in coal and to make as much use as possible of the telegraph in order to rationalise working. 'In a system', said the *Journal des Chemins de Fer*, 'where the steam engine works for only 4 to 5 minutes an hour, it is necessary to produce steam only at the moment and in the quantity necessary for service, if working is not to be rendered ruinous.' For the whole of the year 1849 the company had got working costs down to 2·71 francs per train-kilometre against 4·80 francs in 1847. Operationally, there seems to have been little trouble. The board's report of 1850 to the shareholders says: 'It has never left anything to be desired as regards regularity of service.'

In 1849 the tube was lengthened to run into Saint Germain station, and also it was arranged that the piston carriage should run right through to Paris to avoid the delays in changing traction at Bois de Vésinet. In 1853 the Saint Germain and Rouen companies joined to form the nucleus of the Ouest system. Appropriate homage was paid to the Saint Germain's engineers for their work in building the experimental line, the first hill-climbing locomotive in France, and the iron river bridge, but thereafter the Ouest reports took no interest in the atmospheric railway, nor did the *Journal des Chemins de Fer* mention it, though it continued to be used, in conjunction with some locomotive working also. Then on the evening of 6 September 1858 a train left Saint Germain station and started down the slope. It accelerated, crossed the long viaduct at high speed, and collided with a locomotive in Bois de Vésinet station. There were three dead, including the driver, and several injured. An inquiry showed that the brakes had fractured.

By now it was clear that the increasing number of passengers using the line could be better accommodated by steam engines, and on 3 July 1860 locomotives took over, twenty years and a few days after the Samudas had begun their first tests at Wormwood Scrubs.

The line still exists. It was electrified on the third-rail system in 1927, and now forms part of the Paris suburban network based on the Gare St Lazare. There is no trace of the atmospheric works.

CHAPTER TWELVE

MATTERS OF OPERATION

T HE first chapter described the main features of atmospheric working as they might have been seen by a contemporary. In this, the last, we can glance at some problems it raised and how they were dealt with, always remembering that the period of public working on the two important lines—a little under sixteen months on the London & Croydon, almost twelve on the South Devon—was too short for much development to take place.

THE TUBE

The Dalkey used a 15 in tube; so did the Croydon; The Saint Germain line with its steep incline, one of 25 in. The South Devon intended three sizes, 13 in, 15 in, and 22 in. All three were ordered, but the 13 in was abandoned after a thousand or so had been delivered, and before they were laid. Brunel proposed to invent an expanding piston, and may have done so. Otherwise piston carriages would have had to be changed when the tube size altered. Lengths of tube were socketed into each other, the joints being filled with an oil and wax mixture kept in place by a hempen cord saturated in pitch and hammered home to keep it airtight.

All the engineers mainly concerned—the Samudas, Brunel, Cubitt—failed to foresee the rapid increase in train weights that followed railway development in the forties. The Croydon especially found its potential commuter growth enormous, and by 1847 needed to work rush-hour trains of more than ten coaches up the New Cross incline. Such a weight was well beyond the tractive effort available at 16 in of vacuum. There were four solutions, all undesirable. To increase the tube diameter at very considerable cost; to limit the length of trains and run more of them, which demanded new engines of much great horsepower and larger pumps, able to exhaust the air more quickly; to pump to a higher vacuum, leading to high coal consumption, engine overwork, and increased strain on the continuous valve, or to double the track.

Given that valve leakage greatly increased with every increase in vacuum above 15 in, probably really big tubes and engines, low operating vacuums, and double track were necessary to an intensive commuter service. Samuda had partially realised this by 1846, when he proposed 130 to 150 hp engines and an 18 in tube for the Windsor, Slough & Staines line. But the installation cost would then have been so much higher than that of running locomotives that our ancestors would not have faced it.

Herapath maintained that, quite apart from valve leakage, a great loss of power occurred in a long tube through air friction, which built up as the tube sections were lengthened. 'Before the piston the air cannot get away fast enough, and therefore diminishes the force of the vacuum; and behind it cannot follow up quickly enough to exert its full pressure on the back of the piston.' He considered that theoretically a 15 in piston should yield enough power to propel 220 tons on the level. The practical maximum with leakage at its minimum was less than half this, and he attributed part of the difference to what we should now call viscous drag. In fact this does not seem likely to have been a significant factor.

TUBE OR SEPARATING VALVES

The tube was divided into sections two to three miles long, with short gaps opposite engine-houses, which were usually at stations. Self-acting valves at each end of the tube enabled the piston to leave one section and enter the next without breaking the vacuum. A by-pass tube connected the two main tubes, from which a connection ran to the engine-house. Shut-off valves on the connecting tube and on each side of the by-pass enabled the engines to exhaust either, or if necessary both, sections of the tube, or to cut out the engine-house. Normally, each engine-house exhausted one section of tube, but two sections could if necessary be pumped out from one house, though more time would be needed.

On the Dalkey and Saint Germain line the valves had only to operate in one direction, and because each railway had only one length of tube, they were never passed at high speeds, and worked well enough. On the Croydon and the South Devon a different two-way pattern was used. When tube sections began and ended elsewhere than at stations, or when trains passed certain stations, the valves were given rough treatment by the trains, and seem to have suffered from it. We have, however, little information on what their troubles were.

THE LONGITUDINAL VALVE

The iron strip that held down the valve leather had on the Dalkey line originally been square and sharp-edged, so tending to cut it; later Samuda replaced it with a round iron bar, which was also used elsewhere.

In Samuda's early drawings a hinged weather plate is shown above the valve and protecting it. This was not fitted on the working lines, presumably because it would have been too liable to breakage. Yet it was needed to prevent the valve collecting pebbles and dirt, getting choked with snow, and hardening in frost. Its installation on the South Devon seems to have been one of Samuda's last-minute proposals.

Various kinds of composition were tried. The Dalkey and the Croydon used a mixture of beeswax and tallow, though the latter made a change after the breakdown of May 1846. The South Devon seemingly tried a lime soap which worked well at first, but on exposure to light and air formed a hard skin. To remedy this a mixture of cod oil and soap was tried. It remained soft, but was liable to get sucked into the tube. In the end the Dalkey found that the wet leather maintained the vacuum well enough in ordinary weather without using any composition. Normally the valve leather remained wet and supple, but frost caused it to stiffen, and then it was liable both to leak and be damaged unless treated with very expensive seal oil.

Being a grooveman or man who kept the valve in order was a dangerous job, because of the silent trains. One was killed on the South Devon on 28 May 1848; another, in June, was run over but recovered. A third, who seems to have drunk rather too much, 'had fallen asleep on the Tube while at work', with unpleasant results.

I must now mention the great rat story. Here it is, as given in the 1871 edition of F. T. Buckland's *Curiosities of Natural History*:

> When the atmospheric pump was in use at the terminus of the Croydon Railway, hundreds of rats lost their lives daily. The unscientific creatures used in the night to get into the large iron tube, by exhausting the air from which the railway carriages were put in motion, their object being to lick off the grease from the leather valve, which the engineers of the line were anxious to keep air-tight. As soon as the air-pump was put to work for the first morning train, there was no resisting, and out they were sucked dead corpses.

The spectacle of showers of dead rats sailing out of the air vents of the engine-houses must have been quite a sight for the citizens of Croydon.

As described, it is physically impossible, but probably the story has a substratum of truth; rats may well have licked the composition from the outside of the valve from time to time. But we have to look a good deal further than rats for the cause of failure.

PISTON AND HEATING CARRIAGES

Beneath the piston carriage was an iron bar called the coulter, bolted at its top end to an iron plate fastened to the carriage floor, and at the other running down and then at an angle of some seventy-two degrees past the raised valve to join the piston. The coulter was hung from a universal joint, so that the piston could adapt itself to variations in the tube or track. The pin holding the plate from which the coulter and piston were suspended was designed to break should the piston hit an obstacle. In such a case the junction plate would stay with the piston, and the train would go on.

The inside of the tube was given a smooth covering of tallow in special tallowing sheds before the sections were assembled. This covering soon became polished as the snugly-fitting piston passed down the tube on trial runs. It protruded rather ahead of the leading carriage, was about 15 ft long and shaped like a dumb-bell, its curved leather-covered leading end being connected by a long rod to a leaden counterweight at the back. Behind the piston head, and mounted on top of the rod, were two wheels, the first smaller than the second. These ran on the underside of the iron plates riveted below the valve leather, and by pushing them upwards, broke the beeswax and tallow seal, forced the valve upwards towards its hinge, and held about 15 ft of it open at any one time, so admitting air to the tube. This, rushing into the vacuum, pressed against the back of the piston head and drove it forward.

Behind the two opening wheels was the coulter, which passed along the $1\frac{1}{2}$ in opening between the raised top edge of the hinged valve and the channel of the tube without touching either. And behind that were two more wheels of descending size, to take the weight of the valve until it again lay flat across the slot. Finally, a small sprung steel pressing wheel, hung from the piston carriage (the probable arrangement on the Dalkey and South Devon lines) or from the second or heater carriage (on the Croydon), ran along the top of the valve to push it back into the slot.

Beneath either the piston or the following carriage was suspended a copper rubbing bar about three feet long, which itself was fitted beneath a long iron tube filled with slowly-burning charcoal which kept the bar barely warm. The bar's purpose was to seal the composition after the pressing wheel had pushed the valve back into place, and the heating to prevent the composition sticking to the bar. Should the train stop, however, for long enough for the composition to get hot and melt, a man had to be sent to put in a new supply. A drawing exists of a heater carriage with rubbing bar and pressing wheels that could be raised if the train stopped in the tube : I do not know whether such a type was used.

Some, like M. Mallet, quickly doubted whether this heating had any effect. Bergin, the Dalkey's secretary, thought it did, and said that without it the composition stuck to the rubbing bar, and the valve leakage rate was nearly doubled. Heaters were still being used on the Croydon in August 1846, but later the rubbing bar and its heater were alike dispensed with. In November Samuda wrote : 'we never use the heater and never require it. We find the pressing wheel sufficient.' Heaters were not used on either the South Devon or the Saint Germain lines.

On the Dalkey line, atmospheric working was only upwards from Kingstown, the trains returning by gravity. The piston carriage therefore remained coupled to the Dalkey end of the train. Before it started back, the guard slipped a lever over the square end of a vertical bar passing through the carriage floor, and swung the whole piston assembly to one side, where the bar was hooked. On the downwards journey, therefore, the piston travelled outside the tube. Procedure was very similar on the Saint Germain line, also gravity operated in one direction. On the Croydon and the South Devon, with their two-way working on a single line, it was not possible just to put the piston carriage on a turntable, for then the coulter of the piston would have lain at the wrong angle to enter the space beneath the lifted valve. Oddly enough, there seems to be no evidence of what in fact was done, but the illustration of a piston carriage on the Croydon line reproduced in this book seems to indicate that it was double-ended, and a drawing of a piston on that line which appeared at the time of the tests suggests that the piston head was unscrewed from one end of the bar and screwed on at the other. This would be easier than it sounds, for as the piston head pro-

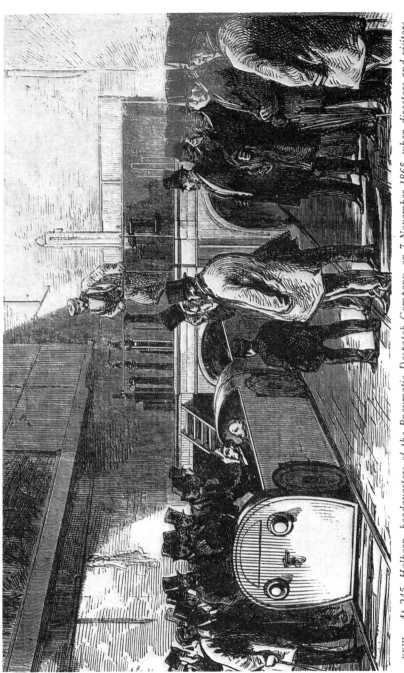

xxiii. At 245, Holborn, headquarters of the Pneumatic Despatch Company, on 7 November 1865, when directors and visitors tested the line to Euston

xxiv. *(above) A car of the Pneumatic Despatch Company, and (below) a portion of the tunnel, formerly under Platform 1 at Euston station*

jected in front of the carriage, no pit would be needed, only a boardwalk between the rails below its level. After removing the nut, which could have been finger-tight and locked with a pin, a two-wheeled trolley could have been used to draw the piston head off its rod and run it to one side, still within the rails, to clear the coulter. The carriage would then be pushed past the trolley and the piston attached at the other end of the rod. The opening wheels would now do the closing, and vice versa.

STARTING

In the first chapter I described the principle on which trains were started on the South Devon, though the details have not come to light. Because of obstructions from sidings, it was often not possible to lay the tube for the starting rope right up to the station. To enable this to be attached, the train had to stop at the end of the platform, and drivers sometimes overshot. As trains could not be backed, passengers had to walk along the line to get on and off. Then plank extensions—called telescopic because they extended over the sidings and could be pulled back—were provided at Starcross and Dawlish. But these were only a few boards wide and, being outside the station roofs, were unpopular with passengers on wet days.

This rope method was far from safe. On 9 November 1847 the rope broke at Starcross when the 3.10 p.m. was leaving the station : 'a man named Drake was struck by the rope and . . . died . . . from the effects of the injuries received', says the company's minute book. On 1 January 1848 a valve man at Teignmouth had his leg so badly broken by a rope parting that it had to be amputated, and on 4 March a rope fell on to the line at Starcross 'whereby the Piston Carriage was thrown off the Line and the Piston much injured'. Pearson, the manager, was asked to put a guide-bar along the platform 'to mark the proper direction for placing the rope'.

Brunel was planning something better, for after this accident he was asked to hurry up and do without towing ropes at Dawlish and Starcross. His alternative was to start trains by using a separate length of full-sized tube about 200 yd long laid through the station, and linked by a connecting pipe to the main tube. Enough power was provided to get the train started. Experiments with this method were being carried out in January 1848, and it may have been that used at Newton from the beginning.

Cubitt had originally intended to start his trains on the Croydon by using a capstan and rope. But instead he so laid the track that it reached an apex in the centre of each station. Trains were stopped just beyond the apex, so that they would re-start by gravity. On the French line a capstan and rope brought trains out of Saint Germain station to the top of the incline. Coming up, as with the improved South Devon method, the piston carriage was held with its piston in an auxiliary tube while the train was coupled up; then, when a valve was opened, the piston moved forward and past the separating valve into the main tube.

SHUNTING

What was not done by using locomotives was performed by hand. On the South Devon, Brunel had originally intended to apply the system already used in the Great Western's goods sheds at Bristol : 'we have several small capstan heads in different parts of the station, which are always in motion running round, and a porter takes a turn round one of these with a rope, which is hooked on to any carriage which he wishes to move'. Power was to be provided by underground shafting from a small steam engine. Imagination boggles at the prospect of elderly passengers getting caught up in the perpetually turning capstans or the tautening ropes; and for children they would have been paradise.

Backing trains was also a difficulty. Brunel had proposed to deal with it by making platforms longer so that precise position did not matter, and by using his capstan. It would have been possible to use the rope starting apparatus, by leading the rope round a pulley and then fastening it to the back of the train, but I do not know whether this was done.

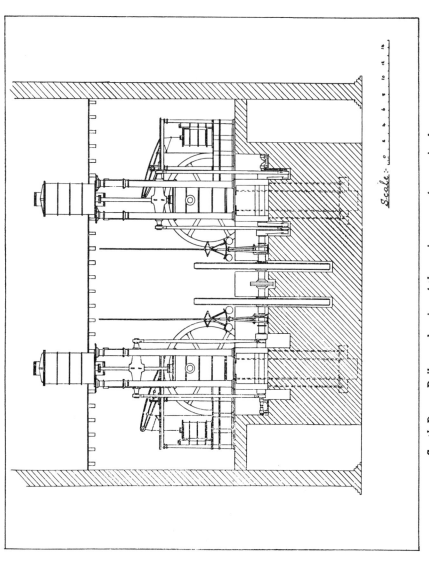

South Devon Railway: drawing of the engine-room of an engine-house

Scale:- 0 2 4 6 8 10 12 14

BRAKING

In early days it was thought likely that atmospheric trains would need more than ordinary brakes to stop in an emergency, or to be held on a steep gradient. On the Croydon it seems that a by-pass valve was fitted to a piston, by means of which air could be passed through to reduce the vacuum in the tube ahead. The control to work it is shown in the plate illustrating the Croydon piston-carriage. This piston was used on test runs, but it seems likely that the brakes proved sufficient, while no-one would want more work to be put on the stationary engines, for nothing more is heard of it on the Croydon or the South Devon. On the Saint Germain line the piston could be dropped if necessary.

The six-wheeled piston carriages and four-wheeled heater carriages of the Croydon line were fitted with a strong cam-operated brake which acted on two brake blocks on each wheel, and was capable of locking them. On the South Devon the braking seems to have been less efficient.

Before the committee on the Croydon & Epsom Bill, Brunel produced the curious argument that locomotives produced such irregularities of the rails and roadbed that it was impossible to fit continuous brakes to a steam-hauled train, in case part of the apparatus might touch the rails or something else. But steel-tyred carriages, suitable for continuous braking could be built and used on an atmospheric line, which could be kept in good order without difficulty.

TRACKWORK

The problem of how to cope with passing places and sidings, for instance to engine-houses, was faced, but hardly solved, by atmospheric railway engineers. Every set of points meant that the tube had to be broken, two more valves inserted, and a by-pass pipe provided. Even then, the piston assembly hanging below the leading carriage was likely to foul any rails crossing the track.

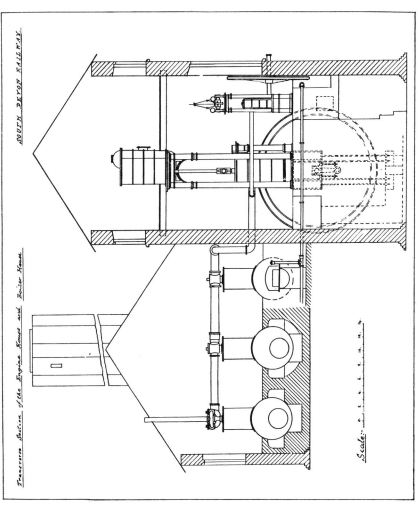

South Devon Railway: sectional drawing of a boiler-house and engine-room

This trouble, like so many others, did not arise on the Dalkey. On the Croydon at Forest Hill the atmospheric line was outside the steam lines. To bring trains to the station platform, to be worked onwards by locomotives, therefore, they had to be switched from one track to another. But this would cause the piston to foul the rails, and therefore Cubitt invented a complicated solution. Two crossings of this design were built and used. They moved not just the points but also the obstructing rails out of the way to give the piston a clear run. Six men had to man the lever that worked each of them, (their total wages were £6 10s a week) until Samuda said, late in the system's life, that he was fitting gearing instead.

The pictures we have of the South Devon suggest that the tube was set higher between the track, so that the piston could normally clear rails crossing its path, though the points for sidings were probably at breaks in the tube. However, a report in the *Mining Journal* of 11 September 1847, (quoting the *Morning Herald*) after saying that there were no Croydon-type switches, goes on: 'by a very simple contrivance the piston is lifted over the ordinary crossing rails with ease and certainly at the highest velocities'. This was a ramp, probably wooden, which lifted the piston over obstructions.

LEVEL CROSSINGS

Several ingenious solutions were proposed for this problem, but it was never in fact solved in practice. There were no level crossings on the Dalkey or the Croydon; on the South Devon, Brunel built an underpass bridge for the Alphington road to avoid one, and was still seeking the right answer for those he would need further down the line when the system closed.

Samuda described to the Select Committee a metal cover, presumably in two sections, over the tube, linked to a piston working in a cylinder connected to it. As exhaustion began, the piston was driven downwards by atmospheric pressure and raised the cover, which then formed a barrier. After the train had passed, the cover fell back by its own weight, and, one surmises, with a

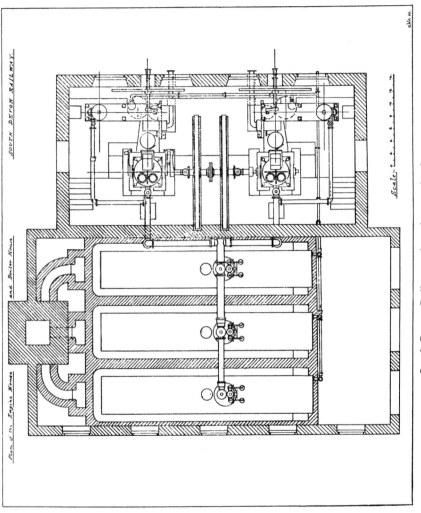

South Devon Railway: plan of an engine-house

bang that would have frightened any waiting horse out of its wits.

To the natural question of a committee about what would happen were a cart to be passing over when the cover began to rise, Samuda replied that the vacuum did not form as quickly as that: the cart would have plenty of time. He seems to have ignored the probable reactions of a horse to the road starting to rise under him.

ENGINE-HOUSES

The engine-houses were architectural monuments to the care of directors that their appearance should not cause hostility. Each usually contained two main steam engines, which could be worked separately or linked together. Several types were used —conventional beam, beam rotative and vertical tandem. Each drove an air-pump, the cylinder generally being double the diameter of the engine cylinder. In three houses on the South Devon Railway, small beam rotative engines were used to drive service pumps of the main plant, otherwise donkey engines worked boiler feed pumps and cranes for lifting coal into the store.

The main pumps took air from the main tube through the connecting pipe, and discharged it to atmosphere. An engine-house contained an engine-room, boiler room, coal store, general store room and water tank, while near it were a siding for coal trucks to stand while they were unloaded, and a reservoir or other means of water supply.

Four men were probably on duty at a time in an engine-house: an engineman, fireman, telegraph operator/lookout man, and a general odd job and valveman. While the first two attended to the engines, the third had to send and receive messages on the early pattern Cooke & Wheatstone electric telegraph machines which provided the only means of communication between one house and the next, and also tell the engineman to stop his engines as soon as a train had passed the house. The fourth man had to operate the valves on the connecting

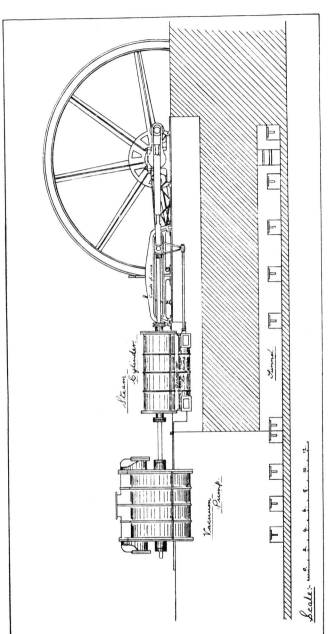

Croydon & Epsom Railway: drawing of a Boulton & Watt 50 hp engine

tube and by-pass, bring up coal, and do the miscellaneous jobs.

Reliable telegraphic links between engine-houses were vital, for efficient working on the longer atmospheric lines depended upon close co-ordination between them. In 1846 the telegraph was in its infancy, though its reputation had been made by the pioneer installation between London and Slough, and it was being installed on a number of railways. The first atmospheric line, the Kingstown & Dalkey in Ireland, had only one engine-house, and opened without the telegraph, though it was put in later. The next, the London & Croydon, opened with three, a fourth never being used. Spelling out its messages letter by letter, the telegraph was used from the start, and seems to have worked well. On the South Devon, however, though it was early installed between stations, it was not completed in all the engine-houses until a month before atmospheric working ended. The stationary engines had therefore to be worked on timetable. This, together with valve defects, caused them to be overdriven and fuel costs to rocket.

THE STATIONARY ENGINES

The longitudinal valve has taken the blame for the failure of atmospheric railways, but at the time the operating superintendents would probably have blamed the engines just as much. We have seen on the Croydon how breakdowns affected train working, and on the South Devon the consequences of a combination of too small a tube, inadequate air-pumps, valve leakage, and lack of a telegraph: engines running too fast for too long at too high a cost.

Four firms supplied pumping machinery that was used on British atmospheric lines—Fairbairn, Maudslay, Rennie, and Boulton, Watt & Co of Soho. A fifth, Harvey & Co of Hayle, provided machinery that was never installed or used. Adequate records survive only to reconstruct the activities of Boulton & Watt, but from what remains it is clear that this firm developed the somewhat unreliable design adapted from foundry blowing

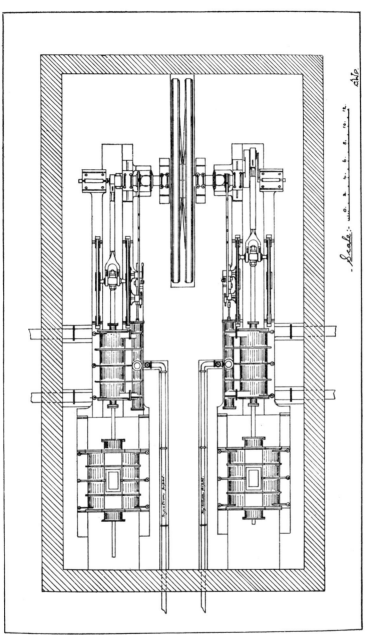

Scale :- [scale markings]

Croydon & Epsom Railway: drawing of two Boulton & Watt 50 h.p. engines arranged to facilitate coupling

engine practice. It is interesting to trace the short history of this firm's atmospheric activities before looking at the layout and characteristics of pumping stations for which they were responsible.

Their first contact with atmospheric railways was in late 1844, when Brunel invited them to tender for some of the plant for the South Devon Railway. Principally involved were Gilbert Hamilton at Soho and H. W. Blake at the London office; Hamilton became an embittered man and disliked Brunel, whom he considered a fraud, whereas Blake seems to have worked closely with him and supplied some of Brunel's engineering knowledge on other projects. Samuda's original specification was for a beam engine of compact design with 33 in × 66in steam and $44\frac{1}{2}$ in × 66 in vacuum cylinders. This was accompanied by two tracings of similar engines, one with an extraordinary connecting rod layout. Hamilton took an immediate dislike to this: 'I see nothing for it but to work out for them their own crudities or at least to stick by them until the Tenders are given out, when the absolute improprieties of construction, such as the working of Samuda's connecting rod . . . may be remonstrated against.' While other makers followed Samuda's design slavishly, Blake and Brunel appear to have got together to design a large table engine, with pump above driven directly by an extension of the piston rod. While this design developed, Hamilton continued to draw up designs based on the original specification, including 12 hp auxiliary engines to work the condenser pumps and to pump water. At the same time he suggested using a standard Boulton & Watt 40 hp* beam engine with the vacuum pump

---

* Most engines, including the Boulton & Watt designs, were described by rated power. This was based on cylinder volume and was taken from standard beam engines of the day, which used steam at lower pressures and ran at lower speeds than the atmospheric pumps; hence the actual power output of the latter was well in excess of the rated figure. The rated powers have sometimes been taken as actual powers, and the conclusion drawn that the engines were too small. Taking the mean effective pressure as 20 psi and the speed as 20 rpm, the indicated horsepowers of the Soho engines would be 124 ($41\frac{1}{2}$ hp type); 148 (50 hp); 269 ($82\frac{1}{2}$ hp), and 244 (68 hp). When these figures are compared with the 110 hp of the Dalkey engine it

beneath the floor and driven from the beam by a double or split rod. Even at this stage the inadequacy of the pumps was noticed, and the bore was increased to 51 in for the first designs. Blake's vertical design was adopted, however, and three pairs were ordered. By the time Boulton's got the order to supply the Croydon & Epsom engines in 1846 a deal of thought had gone into the problem of producing a much improved horizontal engine.

Four pairs of 50 hp and one pair of $82\frac{1}{2}$ hp were ordered; the latter, originally intended for Carshalton, were soon earmarked for New Cross, and construction commenced at once. However, by now the end of the Croydon line was in sight, and in December 1846 the directors asked Boulton's to stop work on the three pairs of engines in hand, compensation of £11,800 being agreed upon. These engines were already made and it was suggested that the New Cross pair be completed and tested. Boulton's, left with parts for a total of five pairs of engines, agreed terms with Samuda whereby he should receive 50 per cent of the profits if he negotiated their sale within two years, and 25 per cent of the same in the following two years; by the time this was signed in September 1847 he had already sold two pairs of 50 hp and the $82\frac{1}{2}$ hp pair to the South Devon, the latter for Dainton and the former for the Torquay branch, thus earning £3,640 commission. The last order was placed in 1846, this for six pairs of 68 hp horizontals for the South Devon Railway. One pair was cancelled later.

The layout of an atmospheric station was similar to that of a waterworks, with the engines in one lofty house set parallel or at right angles to the boilers in their own low-roofed house. The boilers were invariably of Cornish pattern, completely encased in a brick surround filled with ashes. The dome projected above

is evident that the power to length ratios are approximately the same. That the real trouble on the South Devon was the smallness of the pumps is shown by comparing the Dalkey pumps, $66\frac{1}{2}$ in by 66 in and absorbing 78 hp at $22\frac{1}{2}$ rpm, with those on the South Devon verticals, 51 in by 72 in, which on that basis would absorb 55 hp. The engines, having power to spare, were then run much faster than designed—so using much more coal—until at some 35 rpm the power output matched the demands of the pumps.

this, carrying the main steam valve, two safety valves of lever pattern and an anti-vacuum valve to prevent collapse of the boiler when cooling down. The stoking floor was at ground level, with engine floor a little above and sometimes level with the top of the boiler casing. The connecting pipe from the traction tube passed through control valves and entered a large expansion chamber outside the pump house. This chamber, usually made from a strengthened boiler shell, was intended to trap water condensed when the tube was evacuated and was fitted with a weighted flap valve to release condensate. The pipe beyond the chamber divided to feed each pump; the pumps appear from drawings to have exhausted into the engine-house but this seems unlikely, as the noise and heat would have been intolerable with even one engine running at full power. There were normally two engines to each station, these forming a pair which were often run coupled, but each could work independently. Forest Hill had two pairs of engines, as would Carshalton if it had been built. The condensers and other ancillary equipment were under the engine room floor as in normal stationary engine practice.

The engines are worthy of closer study, for although they were developed from blowing engines and were similar in purpose, i.e., they displaced air, certain fundamental differences existed which probably magnified the troubles encountered. To begin with, the compression ratio of a blowing engine would be less than $2:1$, whereas a vacuum pump drawing some 24 in vacuum must have one of at least $5:1$, and under these conditions air will reach temperatures exceeding 100°C. Such temperatures were also encountered in a steam cylinder, but an air pump ran dry, whereas there was always a film of water on the surfaces of a cylinder using non-superheated steam. This was a decade before John Ramsbottom's classic invention of the piston ring, and one can assume that the packings then available would give trouble under such conditions. (It may be noted that the first successful internal combustion engine did not appear until almost immediately *after* this invention.)

Again, the valves of the air-pump, especially the inlet valves, had to be more sensitive and respond to small pressure differences. At Dalkey simple counterpoised flaps were used, which seem to have worked satisfactorily. For the South Devon, outlet valves sprung by indiarubber were tried, and mechanically-operated outlet valves were thought of for the Croydon 50 hp pairs. Finally, reed valves, the best type known at the time, were used for the later pairs, each valve plate having about fifty reeds. Another factor was that a high-compression pump with double-acting cylinder actually drives the engine during the first part of each stroke, while the work per stroke diminishes as the degree of vacuum increases. These last characteristics were responsible for the unusual valve gear of the later engines.

One type of failure during the early stages of running was purely mechanical; the theory of dynamic balance had yet to be stated, and although each engine ran smoothly enough on its own, the torsional stresses involved when two were coupled with cranks at right angles were not then appreciated. The result, as we saw on the Croydon, was fractured couplings; when these were strengthened, the crankshafts themselves broke. This weakness too was allowed for in a rather elegant way on the ill-fated horizontal engines, as will be seen later.

With the irregularities due to these factors added to those produced by inappropriate valve timings, the South Devon Railway verticals ran very roughly and even broke their governors. These were of the correct size, but were subsequently replaced by the most massive available. Perhaps the researches of Fernihough into balancing were stimulated in part by unexpected behaviour in pairs of engines which ran well by themselves? Let us now look at the first and last of the Soho designs; the $41\frac{1}{2}$ hp verticals and the 68 hp horizontals.

The $41\frac{1}{2}$ hp Vertical Engines: South Devon Railway

This imposing design, installed at Exeter, Turf, and Starcross, was an attempt to produce an engine in which the direct coupling of steam and air cylinders gave a layout suited to higher speeds than a beam engine. It must have been something of a disappointment to the makers. The main faults seem to have stemmed from poor valve timing and the coupling together of engines in pairs by a rigid coupling, apart from the vacuum pump troubles that beset everyone.

Each unit stood 27 ft from floor to top of vacuum cylinder, the latter being above the upper floor of the house. The steam cylinder was just above floor level and the columns between this and the vacuum pump also contained the slide bars. From the crosshead, twin connecting rods 16 ft 9in long descended on either side of the cylinder to the crankshaft. On the inner end of the crankshaft was a flywheel of 18 ft 2 in diameter, light in relation to the mass of reciprocating parts. Rather unusually the bores of the steam and air cylinders were not in the ratio 1 : 2, as in normal air-pump practice of the day, being 33 in and 51 in respectively with 6 ft stroke. Slide valves driven by an eccentric controlled steam admission; these had a fixed cut-off and the only control of power output was by main throttle, an inefficient arrangement which also dried the steam to the detriment of packings. Each pair of engines was coupled rigidly by a disc between the flywheels, pins in this coupling permitting the engines to be uncoupled easily. To facilitate starting the main engine, condenser and boiler pumps were driven by a pair of standard 12 hp rotative beam engines installed beside the main plant.

Their poor performance was doubtless a result of inadequate capacity air pumps, these being undersize for engines of their power. Perhaps the pumps were designed for the 13 in tube and never replaced when the diameter was increased. That the engines were of adequate power is evident by their being run fast—underpowered engines cannot be run fast under load.

There were three boilers, each being 35 ft long and 6 ft diameter with an internal flue 3 ft in diameter. The grate had an area of 25 sq ft and heating surface, 610 sq ft. Working pressure was 50 psi(g), the usual 'high pressure' for that period.

Two incidents are worth recounting. When the engines at Exeter were tried out, they ran very roughly indeed : on investigation it was found that on one the connecting rods were of unequal lengths! More bizarre was the first run of a 12 hp engine. These being of standard self-contained design, were built as compactly as possible, and one space-saving idea was to put the governor close to the beam and arrange matters so that the balls swung across the arc of its motion at the end of each stroke. It seems that Joseph Turner, the foreman erector, not having put one of these together before, failed to realise the importance of setting the governor correctly and was most surprised when the balls and beam became entangled on the first stroke!

The big verticals, suffering from crank and coupling break-ages, were further handicapped by the use of cast iron for making certain parts where wrought material was more appropriate—an error on Boulton's part, which followed Maudslay's similar mistakes on the Croydon, and failures were frequent. In mid-1847 the valves were replaced by newer ones having $1\frac{3}{4}$ in lap to give negative lead as on the later horizontals; after this and other modifications had been carried out, they settled down to give quite reliable service, even if they had to be driven hard to compensate for inadequate pumps. At the time of closure they had just been fitted with expansion gear as designed for the later horizontals.

The 68 hp Horizontal Engines: South Devon Railway

A much improved horizontal engine was designed for the Croydon & Epsom line, with a steam cylinder of 36 in and 6 ft stroke, rated at 50 hp. The 72 in vacuum cylinder was driven by an extension on the piston rod of a conventional design, the whole resembling a tandem compound of later years. Large auxiliary engines were not needed, as the engines drove their own condensate pumps; instead, small donkey engines were used to supply the boilers. Piston valves were fitted to the steam cylinder and specially timed. In the original layout each pair of engines was separate, flywheels being on opposite sides with no provision for coupling, but this was amended when the solution to the coupling difficulties was found, and later drawings show the two flywheels adjacent for this purpose. The $82\frac{1}{2}$ hp engines, with

45 in and 90 in diameter steam and vacuum cylinders and 7 ft stroke, were designed this way, and the 68 hp engines for the South Devon Railway extension beyond Newton were a direct development of this type, having certain parts in common. These, the last and most advanced design for the atmospheric railway, were imposing machines with bedplates 57 ft 4 in long and 10 ft 3 in wide under the vacuum cylinder. The steam cylinder was 40 in bore and the air-pump 80 in: stroke was 8 ft. The design of the air-pump followed closely that of earlier practice, but the steam cylinder was greatly improved over the verticals previously described. To begin with, the condenser was set immediately below the steam chest, while the condensate pump for this was mounted under the main cylinder and driven by an extension of the crosshead (similar to the vacuum pump drive on GWR locomotives of later years); the pump had a bore of 13 in and, of course, a stroke of 8 ft. The steam chest was cylindrical and contained piston valves of 13 in diameter with a travel of 14 in; $2\frac{3}{4}$ in steam lap was provided giving $2\frac{3}{4}$ in negative lead but no exhaust lap and hence zero exhaust clearance. This quite extraordinary setting compensated for the air pump driving the engine during the beginning of each stroke; by this means the negative work alone was used to turn the engine past dead centre, the valve admitting steam when the piston was well started on its stroke, thus producing a much smoother turning moment and reducing wear in the bearings.

A very neat expansion gear was designed, for valve gear of normal type would not have permitted the valve timing to remain constant. A double-beat valve, fitted at the inlet to the steam chest, opened at the commencement of each stroke, thus ensuring full pressure when the piston valve opened, and closed at a predetermined point in the stroke to effect expansion. This was more efficient than control by throttle and did ensure wet steam for lubrication. There also was the extra volume of the steam chest to expand at each stroke and to offset this the clearance at the end of the cylinder was cut to a minimum—the piston came to within $\frac{1}{2}$ in of the cover, leaving only about $\frac{1}{2}$ per cent clearance instead of the 5–10 per cent usual on an engine of this size at the time. The expansion valve was operated by a variable sliding cam mounted on a shaft driven at twice engine speed (the valve having to operate twice for each rotation of the crank) and controlled by the governor. This may well have been the first sliding cam valve gear.

Each pair of engines was coupled by an early form of strap drive located between the flywheels; this method reduced torsional oscillation and did not impose the same stresses as did the rigid disc coupling on earlier engines. It could be disconnected easily when the engines were required to run separately. The flywheels were 25 ft diameter, and connecting rods 20 ft long, while the governor stood over 9 ft high.

Steam was supplied by four boilers 30 ft long and 6 ft diameter having a heating surface of 525 sq ft, otherwise they were similar to the earlier design. The engines drove their own condensate pumps, boiler feed being catered for by a separate donkey pump with a 9 in diameter steam cylinder. This arrangement was a definite improvement on what had gone before and one can appreciate the disappointment felt by Boulton's when the $82\frac{1}{2}$ hp engines twice came so near to running and yet were denied the opportunity to prove their worth. Had they been available three years earlier, then perhaps the atmospheric railway would have fared better. Recompense for the effort was to come later when James Watt & Co's layout was adopted for horizontal blowing engines.

Reservoirs were several times proposed as an auxiliary means of exhausting the tube. For instance, it was proposed that a small engine should pump water up to a sealed reservoir connected to the tube; when the head of about 20–25 ft was released, air taking its place would help exhaustion. This idea is linked with Clegg's in his pamphlet of 1839, that receivers should be pumped out by the engines when not at direct work. As we saw, Rammell reverted much later to the same suggestion.

An alternative was put to Brunel by James Nasmyth in March 1845 : the use of low-pressure steam to drive air out of a battery of large vessels, the steam being then condensed in a separate condenser. The exhausted vessels would then be connected to the main tube and draw air from it. Nasmyth thought this method would be cheaper than using steam engines and air-pumps, and would obtain quicker results. He had patented it along with Charles May of Ipswich, but failed to interest Brunel.

And so we come to an end of describing, and explaining, and dissecting. Atmospheric railways were a failure, yet one not far from the elusive boundary of the land of success. Not so far that we cannot play with those eternal words: 'If only. . . .'

APPENDIX

Lines built and projected

(a) Atmospheric lines built and operated

Public services operated between *Kingstown and Dalkey* by the Dublin & Kingstown Railway from 29 March 1844 to 12 April 1854. The line was 1¾ miles long, single-track. One stationary engine at Dalkey. Atmospheric working in one direction only, the other by gravity. Engineer : Charles Vignoles.

Public services operated by the London & Croydon Railway between *Dartmouth Arms (Forest Hill) and Croydon (now West Croydon)* from 19 January 1846. Length 5 miles, single-track. Intermediate stations at Sydenham, Anerley, and Norwood. Stationary engines at Forest Hill, Norwood, and Croydon. Extended for 2½ miles from *Forest Hill* to *New Cross* about 27 February 1847, but engine-house at New Cross not used. All services ended 3 May 1847. Extensions to London Bridge in one direction and Epsom in the other had been authorised. Engineer : William Cubitt.

Public services operated by the South Devon Company between *Exeter St Davids and Teignmouth* from 13 September 1847. Length 15 miles, single-track. Intermediate stations at Exeter St Thomas, Starcross, and Dawlish. Engine-houses at Exeter St Davids, Countess Wear, Turf, Starcross, Dawlish, and Teignmouth. Extended for 5 miles from *Teignmouth to Newton* on 10 January 1848, with engine-houses at Summerhouse and Newton. All services ended on 5 September 1848. Extensions to Plymouth and branch to Torquay (Torre) authorised, and some work done. Engineer : I. K. Brunel.

(b)   Companies that obtained Acts to build lines that could have had atmospheric traction

Cornwall Railway: Plymouth to Falmouth and branches. Bill failed 1845, passed 1846. Engineers : Capt. W. S. Moorsom and I. K. Brunel.

Croydon & Epsom: Act 1844. Associated company, then absorbed by London & Croydon. Engineer : William Cubitt.

Direct London & Portsmouth: From Epsom on the London & Croydon (LBSC) to Portsmouth. Bill failed 1845, passed 1846. Engineer : Joseph Cubitt. Consulting Engineer : William Cubitt.

Dublin & Kingstown: Dalkey to Bray extension. Act passed 1846. Engineer : Charles Vignoles.

South Devon: Torquay (Torre) branch. Act 1845. Engineer : I. K. Brunel.

(c)   Companies that introduced bills to build lines that could have had atmospheric traction

Belfast & Holywood Atmospheric: Along Belfast Lough for about 3 miles. Engineer : C. Lanyon. Petition presented, but bill withdrawn, 1846.

Dublin & Sandymount Atmospheric: 2 miles. Planned as atmospheric line, but went to Parliament as a locomotive line after Sir John Macneill had been made engineer. Bill failed 1846.

Edinburgh & Leith Atmospheric: 2½ miles including branches. Engineer : John Miller. Bill failed 1846.

Exeter, Topsham & Exmouth: From the South Devon at Countess Wear. Engineer : Arthur Whitehead. Bill lost 1846.

Great Kent Atmospheric: London & Croydon Railway to Maidstone and Tonbridge. Engineer : William Cubitt. Bill failed 1846.

Gravesend, Rochester & Chatham: Engineer : I. K. Brunel. Bill failed on Standing Orders, 1844.

Kingstown & Bray: Engineer : Charles Vignoles. Bill failed 1845. Subsequent bill by Dublin & Kingstown Railway succeeded, 1846.

London & Croydon:
(a) from their line to Chatham and Chilham;
(b) from their line to Tonbridge and Maidstone;
(c) Orpington branch.
Bills lost 1845. The second then became the Great Kent Atmospheric. Engineer : William Cubitt.

Northumberland: Newcastle to Berwick. Engineer : I. K. Brunel. Bill lost 1845.

South Devon: Tavistock branch. Engineer : I. K. Brunel. Bills lost 1845 and 1846.

Windsor, Slough & Staines: Engineer : C. Vignoles. Bill lost 1846.

(d) *Some projects and proposals that did not reach the stage of a bill, though sometimes plans were deposited*
Those with a star * proposed atmospheric as a possible system of traction; those with two stars proposed to use it on a portion only of their line; those without a star were atmospheric lines. It should be borne in mind that some projects changed their ideas at different stages in their promotion. The dates given are those of references seen, and are not necessarily the earliest.

London Central Station Companies

City of London Junction: Prelim. notice, June 1845. Cap : £2¼m. A central station behind Moorgate Street and a new Thames bridge. Three stationary engines, one on Surrey side, one at central station, one at Paddington.

General Post Office & Metropolitan Junction: Prelim. notice, October 1845. Cap : £2m. St Martin's le Grand to Islington : branches thence to Camden Town (L & BR) and Paddington (GWR); and by Hoxton to Stepney (Eastern Counties) and the London & Blackwall.

London Railway: Prelim. notice, October 1845. Cap : £5m. Overhead railway connecting termini, and docks on both sides of river.

Thames Embankment & City: Prelim. notice, June 1845. From the LSW at Hungerford Market along a new embankment to Blackfriars, then to the London & Blackwall at Fenchurch Street or the Minories. Advt. August 1845. *Thames Embankment & Atmospheric.* Cap : £2m. Eng : Thomas Page. Hungerford Market to near London Bridge and the Bank, thence to the London & Blackwall, with a branch across the river to London Bridge station. Advt. Sept. 1845. Amalgamated as *Thames Embankment & Railway Junction:* Cap : £1,800,000. Eng : Thomas Page. W. A. Wilkinson a director.

London Suburban Lines

Direct City South Union Atmospheric: Prospectus. Advt. Nov. 1845. Southwark bridge by Kennington to Vauxhall bridge; branch to Old Kent Road near Bricklayers Arms. To be built on a timber viaduct.

Direct Epsom & South London Junction Atmospheric*: Advt. Oct. 1845. Cap : £1½m. Engs : Francis & Alfred Giles. Queen Street, Cheapside, Southwark Bridge, Elephant, Kennington, Mitcham to Epsom. Branches to Bricklayers Arms, Nine Elms, Brixton. Connection to Direct Portsmouth and other lines. See South London Suburban.

Direct London to Gravesend (Pilbrow's Atmospheric): Prelim. notice, Sept. 1845. Cap : £500,000. Eng : F. W. Beaumont. Consulting Eng : James Pilbrow. From near New Cross to Gravesend.

London, Brentford, Hounslow & Great Western Junction*: Prospectus : Cap : £850,000. Eng : Thomas Page. GWR, West Drayton, via Brentford, Hammersmith and Kensington to the Central Terminus near Charing Cross. Later became the *Great Western, Brentford & Central Terminus Junction.*

London & South Essex*: Advt. July 1845. Cap : £900,000. Eng : Joseph Locke. From Stepney on the London & Blackwall to Burnham-on-Crouch, branches to Grays, Tilbury (for Gravesend) and Southend. Atmospheric possibility quickly dropped.

Great Western, Brentford & Central Terminus Junction*:
See London, Brentford, Hounslow & Great Western Junction.

Metropolitan South Suburban Atmospheric: October 1845.

Middlesex & Surrey Grand Junction*: Jan. 1844. Eng : Carl
Tottie. H. de Castro on the board. From Harrow on the
London & Birmingham across the GWR at Southall and the
LSW at Kingston to Merstham on the Brighton and Dover
lines.

North Metropolitan Junction*: Advt. October 1845. Cap :
£900,000. Finsbury Circus to Islington; thence one branch
via Dalston and Northern & Eastern Railway at Tottenham;
other to the London & Birmingham Railway at Camden
Town.

South London Suburban: Advt. May 1845. Cap : £800,000.
Eng : Nathaniel Briant. London Bridge to Camberwell,
branches to Mitcham and Dulwich. Partly on embankment,
partly on viaduct. Withdrawn in favour of the *Direct Epsom
& South London Junction Atmospheric.*

West-end & Southern Counties*: Prospectus. Early 1845.
Cap : £750,000. Eng : J. D. Paine. Waterloo Bridge to Greenwich via Deptford.

Windsor, Staines, Brentford & London Atmospheric*: Advt.
July 1845. Cap : £500,000. Eng : George Rennie. Terminus
near Knightsbridge.

England: South and South East

Brighton & Cheltenham Direct*: Prospectus, 1845. Cap :
£1m. Engs : Sir John Rennie, George Remington. Acting
Eng : Henry Wrigg. Brighton to Andover Road to join proposed Southampton, Manchester & Oxford Junction Railway.

Brighton Junction: Advt. Oct. 1845. Cap : £300,000. Eng :
Charles Blunt. LSW at Guildford to proposed Dorking,
Brighton & Arundel (q.v.), and branch from London &
Brighton Railway. Prospectus, Guildford to Horsham.

Central Kent County*: Advt. Sept. 1845. Prospectus. Cap :
£1½m. Eng : J. W. Bazalgette. Consulting Eng : John Braithwaite. London & Croydon Railway, near New Cross, via
Bromley to Maidstone and Ashford; branch to Tonbridge.

Direct Independent Kent, Surrey & Sussex Union: Prospectus. London, Borough, to Camberwell : one branch to Maidstone, the other towards Horsham.

Direct London & Hastings*: Advt. Oct. 1845. Cap : £1m. Engs : (acting) : W. Rider, George Smith. Croydon via Tunbridge Wells to Hastings, branches to Lewes and Rye.

Dorking, Brighton & Arundel Atmospheric: Prospectus. Advt. Oct. 1845. Cap : £1m. Eng : Charles Vignoles. Dorking, junction with Direct London & Portsmouth, to Brighton; branch from Horsham through Pulborough to Arundel. Plans dep.

Dorking & Reigate: Early 1845 or earlier.

Herne Bay, Canterbury & Faversham Junction Atmospheric: Prelim. notice, Oct. 1845.

London & Chatham and Chatham & Portsmouth Junction: Prospectus June 1844. Cap : £1m. Eng : I. K. Brunel. From the London & Croydon to Chatham; branch to LSW at Esher. An associate of the London & Croydon company. Dropped 1845 in favour of L & C's own bills.

Ramsgate & Margate: Dec. 1843.

Reading & Reigate Atmospheric: Prospectus, 1845. Cap : £800,000. Eng : (acting) : Sandiforth F. Griffin. GWR at Reading to LSW at Farnborough and to Dorking, Reigate and Redhill, for SER and London & Brighton. Earlier called the *Devonport, Bristol & Dover Junction*, then the *Reading, Reigate & Dover*, then the *Reading & Reigate Junction*.

England: South West

Great Western Extension Atmospheric: Advt. Aug. 1845 as Great Western Extension, no mention of atmospheric. Advt. Sept. 1845. Cap : £950,000. Eng : John Taylor. Exeter to Ilfracombe, branches to Bideford and Southmolton.

North Devon*: 1844. Cap : £400,000. Eng : I. K. Brunel. Crediton to Barnstaple. By July 1845, grown to bigger scheme, and atmospheric possibility dropped.

Somersetshire & North Devon Junction*: Advt. Oct. 1845. Cap : £1½m. Eng : John Hughes. Consulting Eng : Charles Fox. Bridgwater via Minehead to Ilfracombe (for Ireland); branch to Barnstaple.

England: North & North East

Leeds & Bradford Direct (Atmospheric): Prospectus, Jan. 1846. Cap : £250,000. Eng : (acting) : Hamilton Fulton.

Leeds & Edinburgh Direct Atmospheric: Advt. Oct. 1845. Cap : £3,300,000. 'Through extensive mining districts of Grassington, Arkendale, Swaledale, Middleton in Teesdale, Weardale, Alston Moor, Blanchland, and Allendale . . . Haydon Bridge . . . across Newcastle and Carlisle (Railway), through mineral district of North Tyne, and then to Edinburgh'.

Leeds & Thirsk: Nov. 1845. Extensions to Pateley Bridge and Knaresborough. Eng : Thomas Grainger.

Leeds & West Riding Junction**: BoT report, Feb. 1845. Leeds to Manchester & Leeds Railway via Pudsey, Low Moor, and Halifax; Bradford to Low Moor; Leeds to Dewsbury; M&LR at Cooper's Bridge to Huddersfield; and branches. Atmospheric traction on 1 in 60 inclines each side of summit only. Eng : John Hawkshaw.

Manchester, Hebden Bridge & Keighley Junction*: Advt. Oct. 1845. Via Haworth.

Manchester, Leeds & York Direct Atmospheric: Plans dep., 1845.

Wakefield, Ossett & Dewsbury Direct & Atmospheric: Advt. Nov. 1845. Cap : £120,000. Eng : James Murphy. Consulting Eng : Charles Vignoles.

England: North West and West Midlands

Liverpool, Warrington, Manchester & Stockport Direct: 1845. Cap : £1m. Connects at Manchester with the Direct London & Manchester. Branch to Stockport.

Manchester & Bury Atmospheric: Advt. Oct. 1845. Cap : £200,000. Eng : Joseph Samuda. Plans dep. Nov. 1845. From Hunt's Bank, Manchester to Market Place, Bury.

Oldham, Manchester, Liverpool & Birkenhead Junction*: Advt. Oct. 1845. Cap : £700,000. Eng : G. P. Bidder. Oldham to join Huddersfield & Manchester Railway. Also Stretford on South Junction Railway to Warrington, GJR.

Rochdale, Heywood & Manchester: Nov. 1845. Eng : Joseph Samuda. A branch of the Manchester & Bury Atmospheric.

England: East and East Midlands

Great Grimsby, Sheffield, the Potteries & Grand Junction*: Advt. Oct. 1845. Cap : £1¾m. Eng : John Fowler. Sheffield via Potteries to Grand Junction Railway at Madeley.

London & Norwich Direct: Originally non-atmospheric. Advt. Oct. 1845. Eng : Joseph Samuda. Via Dunmow and Bury St Edmunds; branches to West Essex, Great Yarmouth and King's Lynn.

England: Central Lines

Cooke's National: Prospectus. Cap : £40m. Eng : William R. Cooke. London to Edinburgh; Exeter; Hull; Shrewsbury; Gloucester; and branches. Broad-gauge, Prosser's system.

Direct Birmingham, Oxford, Reading & Brighton*: Advt. Sept. 1845. Cap : £2m. Eng : Charles Vignoles. Birmingham, Oxford, Reading, Farnborough and Horsham to Brighton.

Direct London & Dublin (Pilbrow's Atmospheric): Prelim. notice, Sept. 1845. Birmingham (L&BR) via Shrewsbury to the Chester & Holyhead Railway at Bangor.

Direct London & Holyhead, and Port Dynllaen*: Advt. Sept. 1845. Cap : £2½m. Engs : Joseph Gibbs, Arthur Dean. Shrewsbury via Bala to Chester & Holyhead Railway at Bangor; also Bala to Portmadoc and Port Dynllaen.

Direct London, Manchester & York (Remington's Line)*: Prospectus, 1844. Cap : £7m. Eng : George Remington. Lines to Manchester and York, branching near Bedford. Dropped in favour of

Direct London & Manchester (Remington's Line)*: Prospectus. Prelim. notice, May 1845. Advt. Oct. 1845. Cap : £3m. Eng : Sir John Rennie.

Great Eastern & Western*: May 1845. Cap : £3½m. Eng : William Gravatt. Great Yarmouth to Swansea.

London & Northampton Direct Atmospheric: Prelim. notice, Nov. 1845. Principally along the roads, the line being screened from sight of the horses.

Ireland

Dublin & Galway Grand Canal & Railway: Prospectus, 1845. Eng : Joseph Cubitt. Consulting Eng : William Cubitt.

Dublin & Baltinglass: Oct. 1845.

Grand Canal Atmospheric: August 1843 to 1845. Dublin to Sallins. Superseded by the Dublin & Galway Grand Canal & Railway.

Irish North Western*: Prospectus, 1845. Dublin to Sligo.

Newry & Castleblaney: Prelim. notice, Oct. 1845. Cap : £200,000. To join Dundalk & Enniskillen Railway at Castleblaney.

Scotland

Leeds & Edinburgh Direct Atmospheric: See p. 219.

Scottish Grand Junction**: 1845. Eng : George Marton. Certain gradients of 1 in 40 at the head of Loch Lomond to be worked by atmospheric traction.

Wales

Great Eastern & Western*: See p. 220.

Great Welsh**: Advt. July 1845. Cap : £4m. Bangor to Pembroke via Shrewsbury, Hereford and Merthyr Tydfil. Later the *Great Welsh Junction.*

Great Welsh Central*: Advt. Sept. 1845. Cap : £2½m. Eng : John A. Galloway. Swansea via Llandovery to Oswestry and Runcorn; branch to Brecon.

Direct London & Dublin (Pilbrow's Atmospheric)*: See p. 220.

Direct London & Holyhead, and Port Dynllaen*: See p. 220.

(a)   Atmospheric lines built and operated

Public services operated by the Compagnie du Chemin de Fer de Paris à Saint Germain between *Bois de Vésinet and Saint Germain* from 24 April 1847 to 2 July 1860. The line was 1⅜ miles long, single-track, with atmospheric working in one direction only, the other being by gravity. One engine-house at Saint Germain. Engineer, Eugène Flachat. Extension authorised for 4 miles to Nanterre. Engine-houses built, but no service worked.

(b)   Projects

There were many of these, and only a few are noted here :

France
Paris—Meaux, 1844; Versailles—Saint Cyr, 1845; Bourg la Reine—Orsay, 1845. La Villette—Sevran, 1845; Paris & Lyons Rly. at Vaise over the Saone to Croix Rouge and the port of Saint Clair, 1846; Paris to Passy, Auteuil and Boulogne village, and also a barge line from St Cloud to St Nicholas quay, Paris, 1846.

Belgium
Brussels—Louvain, 1845-6.

Germany
Berlin—Charlottenburg, 1844. Altona to the Elbe, 1845.

Austria-Hungary
On the Semmering line**, 1844-45; Vienna—Schönbrunn, 1845.

Italy
Genoa—Turin**, mountain section, 1842; Italian & Austrian Railway, Verona to Ancona, 1844.

West Indies
Jamaica, Milk River to Montego Bay (Pilbrow's), 1845; Southern, Eastern & Northern Railway*, 1845.

Antigua, Antigua Railway*, 1845.

BIBLIOGRAPHY

The following are the principal sources :

'Anglo Scot'. 'An Irish Atmospheric Railway', *Railway Magazine*, 1907.

Arago, D. F. J. *Mons. Arago's Report on the atmospheric railway system*, London, 1844.

Barlow, P. W. *Comparative advantages of the atmospheric railway system; with an appendix containing experiments on the Tyler Hill plane of the Canterbury & Whitstable Railway*, London, 1845.

Beach, Alfred E. *The Pneumatic Dispatch*, U.S.A., 1868.

Becker, F. *Atmospharische Eisenbahnen: nach den Berichten von Smith, Mallet, Samuda, Pim, usw., und englischen Quellen bearbeitet*, Frankfurt-am-Main, 1844.

Bergéron, Charles. *Les Chemins de fer Pneumatiques*, 1864.

Bergin, T. F. *The Atmospheric Railway: observations on the report of Lieut-Col. Sir Frederick Smith and Professor Barlow on the atmospheric railway, addressed to Francis Low, Esq., chairman of the Dublin and Kingstown Railway Company*, Dublin, 1843.

Bramwell, Sir Frederick, Bt. 'The South Devon Atmospheric Railway'. *(Proc. Inst. Mech. Engs.)* July, 1899.

Clayton, Howard. *The Atmospheric Railways*, 1966.

Clegg, S. *Clegg's Patent Atmospheric Railway*, London, 1839.

Clegg, S. and Samuda, J'A. *Clegg and Samuda's Atmospheric Railway*, London, 1840.

(Cole, H.) *Railway Chronicle Travelling Charts: The London & Croydon Railway*, London (1846).

Day, John R. and Wilson, B. G. *Unusual Railways*, London, 1957.

Dubern, H. A. *De l'application de l'air atmosphérique aux chemins de fer: resumé des opinions des ingénieurs français et anglais sur les chemins de fer atmosphériques*, Paris, 1846.

Gill, Thomas. *Address to the proprietors of the South Devon Railway, by the Chairman of the Board of Directors*, London, 1848.

Hallette, A. *Tube propulseur-Hallette: systeme d'exècution d'exploitation des chemins de fer par la pression atmosphérique*, Batignolles, (1844).

Hebert, L. *The Engineer's and Mechanic's Encyclopaedia*, London, 1836.

Hewlett, J. G. *On atmospheric traction in general, with explanations and illustrations of Pilbrow's atmospheric railway and canal propulsion*; being the substance of a paper read before the Society of Arts, March 19, 1845.

Hubbard, G. *Cooke and Wheatstone*, London, 1965.

Irwin, G. O'M. *The Illustrated Hand-Book to the County of Wicklow*, London, 1844.

Jones, W. *A popular sketch of the various proposed schemes of atmospheric railway* . . . being the substance of lectures delivered at the Royal Adelaide Gallery in . . . February 1845.

Kirkland, R. K. 'The Waterloo & Whitehall Railway', *Railway Magazine*, 1955.

Lillie, Sir J. S. *Suggestions for improvements in railway travelling by atmospheric pressure*, N.D.

Macneill, Sir J. B. *Atmospheric Railway. Report of Sir John Macneill to the provisional committee of the Great Southern & Western Railway, Ireland, and letter from the chairman to Mr. Pim*, (Dublin, 1844).

Macneill, Sir J. B. *Reports . . . to the provisional committee of the Dublin & Cashel Railway*, Dublin, 1844.

Mallet, R. *Report of the Institute of France upon M. Arnollet's system of atmospheric railways*, Dublin, 1845.

Mallet, R. *Report on the railroad constructed from Kingstown to Dalkey in Ireland upon the atmospheric system, and upon the application of this system to railways in general*, (Paris, 1844).

Medhurst, George. *A new method of carrying letters and goods with great certainty and rapidity by air*, London, 1810.

Medhurst, George. *Calculations and remarks tending to prove the practicability, effects and advantages of a plan for the rapid conveyance of goods and passengers upon an iron road through a tube of 30 feet in area by the power and velocity of air*, London, 1812.

Medhurst, George. *A new system of inland conveyance for goods and passengers.* London, 1827.

Miller, Joseph. *Statistics of Railways: No. 2. London & Croydon Railway 1846.*

Murray, Kevin. 'The End of the Atmospheric Railway', *Railway Magazine*, 1954.

Murray, Kevin. 'The Atmospheric Railway Episode', *Journal of the Irish Railway Record Society*, Spring, 1954.

Ottley, George. *A Bibliography of British Railway History*, London, 1966.

Pilbrow, James. *Atmospheric railway and canal propulsion, and pneumatic telegraph*, London, 1844.

Pim, James. *The atmospheric railway: a letter to the Earl of Ripon, President of the Board of Trade*, London, 1841.

Pim, James. *Irish Railways. The atmospheric railway: a letter to Viscount Morpeth*, London, 1841.

Pinkus, Henry. *Prospectus of a New Agrarian System*, London, 1840.

Pinkus, Henry. *The Pneumatic-Atmospheric and Gaso-Pneumatic Railway, Common Road and Canal Transit*, London, 1840.

Rammell, T. W. *A New Plan for Street Railways*, London, 1857.

Ricardo, M. *A letter addressed to Dr. Yates on the proposed plan of travelling by atmospheric pressure*, Brighton, 1827.

Samuda, J'A. *A treatise on the adaptation of atmospheric pressure to the purposes of locomotion on railways*, London, 1841.

Shearman, D. T. 'Some Atmospheric Railways', *Railway Magazine*, 1909.

Smith, Sir Frederick, and Barlow, Prof. *Report . . . to the . . . Earl of Ripon, President of the Board of Trade, on the atmospheric railway*, London, 1842.

Sowerby, W. *Description of Harlow & Young's patent atmospheric railway, with observations on the atmospheric system*, London, 1848.

Stephenson, Robert. *Report on the atmospheric railway system*, London, 1844.

Thompson, Harry. 'London's Lost Tunnel', *Windsor Magazine*, April 1900.

Turnbull, W. *An Essay on the Air-Pump and Atmospheric Railway*, London, 1847.

(Vallance, John) *On Facility of Intercourse*, London, 1824.

Vallance, John. *A letter to M. Ricardo, Esq., in reply to his letter to Dr. Yates on the proposed method of pneumatic transmission by atmospheric pressure*, Brighton, 1827.

Vallance, John. *A letter to the Kensington Canal Company, on the substitution of the pneumatic railway for the common railway*, London, 1833.

Vifquain, A. *Chemin de fer atmosphérique de Bruxelles a Louvain*, 1846.

Vignoles, O. J. *Life of Charles Blacker Vignoles,* 1889.

―― Boulton & Watt records, Birmingham PL : portfolios of drawings 669, 670, 674; firm's letter-books Jan. 1845―July 1851; foundry order books, Dec. 1839―Nov. 1853; foundry letter-books Feb. 1844―March 1849; letter boxes 10, 18, 44 (1844-7).

―― *Dublin and Kingstown Railway. Return. House of Commons,* 28 February 1843.

―― 'Pneumatic Despatch', *St. James's Magazine,* III, 1862. *Pneumatic Tubes and Telegram Conveyors,* Post Office Green Paper No. 9, 1935.

―― *Report of the Select Committee (House of Commons) appointed to inquire into the merits of the Atmospheric System of Railway,* 22 April 1845.

―― *Report of the Committee appointed by the Postmaster-General to consider the question of the transmission of mails in London by pneumatic tubes or underground electric railways,* February 1911.

Minutes of the Proceedings of the Institution of Civil Engineers, Files of *Bradshaw's Railway Gazette, The Engineer, Engineering, Herapath's Railway & Commercial Journal, Mechanics Magazine, Mining Journal, Railway Chronicle, Railway Herald, Railway Magazine* (Herapath's), *Railway News, Railway Record, Railway Times, The Times, Illustrated London News, Pictorial Times, Exeter Flying Post, Woolmer's Exeter & Plymouth Gazette, Western Times, L'Illustration.*

Records in British Transport Historical Records of the London & Croydon, London, Brighton & South Coast, South Devon and Direct London & Portsmouth Railways; with Coras Iompair Eireann of the Dublin & Kingstown Railway; in the Post Office Records Office.

Collections of railway prospectuses, British Transport Historical Records and British Museum Map Room.

ACKNOWLEDGEMENTS

May I thank Mr C. P. and Mr C. R. Weaver for the research they did for me on the Boulton & Watt records, Mr C. P. Weaver for drawing figures 11 to 15, and Mr C. R. Weaver for contributing the section on stationary engines in Chapter XII; Mr Peter Martin for much engineering help; M. François Caron for doing the research upon which Chapter XI is based; Mr Charles E. Lee for lending me his files; Mr John Hollingsworth for lending me some of Samuda's letters; Mr Kevin Murray for lending me his notes on the Dalkey line and reading the appropriate sections of the book, and Mr L. T. C. Rolt and Mr C. R. Weaver for reading and commenting on the draft manuscript?

My grateful thanks are also due to the staffs of British Transport Historical Records, the Institution of Civil Engineers, the House of Lords Record Office, the British Museum, the Post Office Records Office, the Patent Office, and many public libraries; to members of the Samuda family; to Professor T. C. Barker; Mr D. W. Blackmore; Mr C. R. Clinker; Professor F. Crouzet; Sir Arthur Elton, Bt; Dr W. A. McCutcheon; Mr George Ottley; Mr H. W. Paar; Mr J. Foster Petree; Mr David St J. Thomas; Mr Edward Treby, and all those others who have so kindly helped me.

I am grateful to the following for allowing me to use illustrations : Institution of Civil Engineers (photo W. H. R. Godwin), plate 1(a); Mr Charles E. Lee, plates 1(b), 2(c), 6(a), 8(b), 9(a), 9(b), 10; British Transport Historical Records (photos British Railways, WR), plates 2(a), 2(b), 3(a), 7(a), 11(a), 11(b), 12(a), 12(b), 13(a), 13(b), 14(a), 14(b), 15(a), 16(a), 16(b), 18(a), 18(b), 19(a), 19(b), 19(c), 22, 23; (photo, British Railways, LMR) figure 8; Mr Kevin Murray, plates 3(b), 3(c), 4(a), 4(b), 5(a), 5(b); the British Museum, plates 6(b), 8(a), fig 2; Mr D. W. Blackmore, acting Water Engineer and Manager, London Borough of Croydon (photo G. Hana Ltd) plate 7(b); British Railways, WR Deeds & Records (photo British Railways, WR) fig 6; A. P. & M. Jacobs, plate 17; Sir Arthur Elton, Bt (photo F.C.P. Studios), plate 15(b); L'Illustration (photos Bibl Nat Paris), plates 20, 21, fig 10; British Railways, LMR, plates 24(a), 24(b); Mr C. P.

Weaver, figs 11-15; Mr John Goodchild and the West Riding County Record Office, fig 1; Mr John Hollingsworth, fig 5.

Plates 1(b), 2(c), 6(a), 8(b), 9(a), 9(b), 10, are from the *Pictorial Times*; plates 3(a), 7(a), 22, 23, from the *Illustrated London News*, plates 20, 21 and fig 10 from *L'Illustration*, plates 6(b) and 8(a) from *Railway Travelling Charts (London & Croydon)*.

Finally, my thanks are due to my secretary, Mrs C. M. Halford, for typing so many drafts of the manuscript, my wife for her advice and patience, and my publisher for his encouragement.

CHARLES HADFIELD

INDEX

229